CW00553304

PAGE 12

PAGE 26

PAGE 42

FICTION

COVER IMAGE: SHUTTERSTOCK

PAGE
72

PAGE
136

PAGE
165

CELEBRITY

BRAINBOOSTERS

COOKERY

They've Got The **JOY** Factor!

We've rounded up a warm and fuzzy bunch of celebrities who have truly mastered the art of making us feel good…

A true comedy icon, Dawn French (67) never fails to bring joy, whether we're watching vintage episodes of the award-winning *Vicar Of Dibley* or enjoying one of the many brilliant *French and Saunders* sketches from the 1980s.

A unique blend of infectious humour, razor-sharp wit and warmth infuse all of Dawn's performances and interviews, and her down-to-earth attitude strikes a chord with every fan.

When she decided to abandon her trademark glossy black bob and embrace the grey a few years ago, she made us all smile when she admitted cheerfully in an interview that "all the money saved on hair dye is instead spent on pasties".

She created real magic on the small screen with friend and fellow comedian Jennifer Saunders when they introduced the TV series, *French and Saunders*, which gave us some of the most memorable and funny sketches ever to hit our TV screens.

Who could forget their *Gentlemen Prefer Blondes* sketch where Dawn channelled her inner Hollywood goddess, striding onto stage as Jane Russell? Or that incredibly funny *Titanic* scene?

The next decade brought us *The Vicar of Dibley* where Dawn took on the lead role of Geraldine Granger. Running for just three series, the show was a massive hit and brought us more iconic laugh-out-loud moments – we'll never forget that moment when Geraldine fell in the puddle!

Dawn has also brought the bookworms among us great happiness, having penned four bestselling novels. The latest, *Because Of You,* was longlisted for the 2021 Women's Prize For Fiction. Dawn's autobiography, *Dear Fatty*, which charted her incredible rise to fame, was loved by her fans.

The good news is that there's plenty more to come from Dawn. A new sitcom is in the works and is expected to land on our screens soon. ➡

Sharing a laugh on *This Morning*

Dawn is equal
parts glamour
and warmth

JANE McDONALD

Jane's a joyful force to be reckoned with at every turn, whether that's trading hilariously saucy double entendres while cooking up a storm in the kitchen with Gino D'Acampo or taking a trip down memory lane with her fellow Loose Women.

However, nothing makes us feel quite so filled with joy as when we've watched an episode of *Cruising With Jane McDonald* or another of her travel shows that has seen her explore everywhere from Japan to the Canary islands.

From the moment she utters her first "Hiya, luv!" to the eagerly anticipated song at the end of each show, Jane never fails to make us smile.

**Chatty Jane is
full of fun**

Hannah's enthusiasm is infectious

HANNAH WADDINGHAM

Glorious with a capital G, Hannah Waddingham has shot to stardom in recent years, astounding us with her infectious enthusiasm, good humour and stunning acting and singing talent.

She first really came to our attention on the hit feel good show *Ted Lasso*, where she played business woman and owner of AFC Richmond, Rebecca Welton, but since then she has entertained us with her memorable Eurovision hosting duties and the *Hannah Waddingham: Home For Christmas* Apple TV show where she got us all well and truly in the Christmas spirit, appearing on stage in a flurry of sequins and belting out loads of sing-along festive favourites.

Sir Ian has some close-knit friends

SIR IAN McKELLEN

With a career spanning six decades, Sir Ian's spellbinding performances in everything from Shakespeare to *Lord Of The Rings* never fail to move us. But it's listening to his wonderful anecdotes that brings us real joy, the stories of his enduring bromance with Patrick Stewart and his impressions of fellow actors – we especially loved his Maggie Smith impression on *The Graham Norton Show*!

In a bizarre but truly joyful turn of events, Sir Ian has formed a firm friendship with Bjorn Ulvaeus from Abba over a passion for knitting – they post videos online and even plan to create stagewear for Kylie Minogue! ➡

MIRIAM MARGOLYES

Fabulously forthright and brutally honest,
watching Miriam Margolyes is always a
treat – especially as nobody ever really
knows what's coming next! In a world
filled with rules, it's refreshing to watch
someone like Miriam whose mission in
life is to break all of them.

Highly intelligent and articulate,
Miraim is self-admittedly "very naughty"
too. Her complete fearlessness when
it comes to saying it how it is has led
to some golden TV moments for us to
giggle over, as Miriam turns the full
force of her mischievous charm on her
unsuspecting fellow guests on talk
shows – or even the presenters – often
with hilarious results.

Watch out, Alison's about...

ALISON HAMMOND

As soon as you hear that Brummie accent followed by peals of laughter, you know it's not long before you're going to be howling with laughter at whatever latest fix Alison Hammond has found herself in. Since she first burst onto our screens as a contestant on *Big Brother* in 2002, she's kept us constantly entertained during stints on everything from *The Great British Bake Off* to *This Morning*. The latter has seen her interview some of the world's biggest stars with varying outcomes – we loved watching Harrison Ford dissolve into a giggling fit during his interview and also when she "married" Dwayne Johnson. However, nothing can quite top the moment she accidentally catapulted a topless sailor into the Thames!

ANTON DU BEKE

He's dancing royalty and a true entertainer – one whose passion shines through in every performance. We loved his good-humoured performances on *Strictly* when teamed with everyone from Ann Widdecombe to Judy Murray. We cheered in series 17 as he finally received his first 10s, from Bruno Tonioli and Shirley Ballas, following a dance with that year's partner, Emma Barton. Anton thoroughly entertains us as a judge on *Strictly* nowadays and always seems to find a positive spin for each performance. Thanks to his enthusiasm, talent and dance knowledge, he really brings joy to every *Strictly* show! 🆆

Anton brings the feel good factor

Wine O'Clock

Lexie was looking to the future – and this Dry January challenge was going to be a breeze…

By Tess Niland Kimber

Lexie was glad to see the end of 2023 for several reasons, she thought as she transferred key dates to the new calendar.

It had been a tough year. Sadly there had been the break-up with Ed, then moving to this Portsmouth flat and settling Scarlett and Nate in new schools.

Work at Home Sweet Home had been demanding, too. Winter was the house maintenance firm's busiest period with boiler repairs, roof leaks and double-glazing requests.

Funnily enough, it had been through Home Sweet Home that she'd met Ed, a gas fitter. The more work she offered, the more they chatted on the phone until he asked her out.

he didn't always display them himself.

Why couldn't they at least be friends? They'd once loved each other very much.

Lexie gave the client's address and the call ended, leaving her rattled. Their conversations were always like this now and she'd pick over his words, searching for a grain of warmth.

"I think you're still hung up on him," her best friend Tom would say. "In fact, I think he still loves you, too. That's why he's so grouchy."

Tom had his own relationship problems with partner Paul, and they'd often drown their sorrows over a bottle of red when Ed had the children.

"I don't think so!" she said, too vehemently to be convincing.

Tom had raised a perfectly waxed

Why couldn't they be friends? They'd once loved each other very much

Ed still worked for Home Sweet Home, which proved increasingly awkward. As it had done yesterday…

"When do you want me to go?" he'd sighed down the phone.

"As soon as possible. Mrs Glover has no hot water and two children under ten."

There'd been a pause, then Ed had sighed again.

"OK. I'll go this afternoon. Address?"

Lexie had pursed her lips. Had he always been this abrupt?

She only hoped that when he had the children he taught them good manners, if

eyebrow. "Make peace with him. Then you'll make peace with yourself."

"I'd like to," she admitted, curling into Tom's squashy sofa. "But Ed makes it difficult. Just booking him in for a job makes my blood boil. And when he collects the children, he's always late or miserable."

Tom tipped his head. She knew what he was thinking, but he was wrong. They were over. Ed was a big pain, but she couldn't say goodbye to him as they had a lifelong connection through the children.

"At least he's a good dad." ➡

"He's a great dad," she'd admit, usually halfway through her second glass.

Now, as Lexie hung the calendar above the fridge, she realised nights with Tom would soon change. She'd taken the plunge. Dry January was here.

L exie didn't consider herself much of a drinker, so the Dry January challenge should be a doddle.

OK – after a hard day she looked forward to wine o'clock. And if Ed had the children to stay, then drinks with the girls on Saturday nights were fun and Sunday roasts at The White Hart weren't the same without Malbec.

Even when she met Mum in town for a cream tea, they'd enjoy the prosecco deal.

In fact, it had been Mum who'd asked her on Christmas Day, "So – how will you cope?"

Ed had the children, so they were "celebrating" Lexie's first Christmas in the apartment, but the atmosphere was as flat as a Shrove Tuesday pancake.

Scarlett and Nate would be here tomorrow and over New Year, but it had been awful waking up without them. And – if she was honest – without Ed, too. He was a real festive season junkie.

Briefly, she allowed herself to remember previous years with Ed sitting in the armchair wearing his Christmas jumper and the paper party hat he simply refused to take off, while putting together endless toys for the children, before he'd carved the turkey.

This year it was just her and Mum. Relaxing, but way too quiet.

"Cope? With what?"

"Dry January, of course."

"Oh, fine. I don't drink much," she'd said.

"Don't you?" Mum frowned. "But you drink most evenings."

"Most," she agreed, while mentally admitting it was every evening – but only a glass or two. She wasn't a binge drinker.

Besides, wasn't red wine supposed to be good for you? All those lovely antioxidants…

"And you never, ever take the car when you go out."

"No. I book taxis."

"Because," Mum reached for a mince pie, "you'll be over the limit."

"Yes, but I only go out occasionally. I'm hardly on the liver transplant list."

Mum fixed her with her warm brown gaze. Was she concerned?

"No, but you drink more than you think. Ed hated it."

They fell silent as the National Anthem played, but Lexie couldn't concentrate on the King's words.

Mum was wrong. She wasn't a heavy drinker. Dry January would be easy.

She'd show her.

The first day proved incredibly hard, but was that due to the hangover from the night before.

New Year's Eve had been a blast with a fancy-dress night at the pub. Dressed as a cowgirl, she'd met someone. A man called… Well, she couldn't remember his name, but he'd been nice.

she poured herself an orange juice, she felt ratty. She'd been looking forward to opening the Shiraz.

Throwing the dice, she decided Dry January was like dieting. Whenever she counted the calories, she'd crave chocolate cake because she couldn't have it. Now she was grimly determined to stick to her drinking "diet."

The next night was harder. After the kids went to bed, she checked the clock a dozen times. She felt restless.

Once she'd even reached for a glass. Who would know? The children very rarely got up at night.

But that would be cheating…

Instead, she made a hot chocolate and, scrolling through the channels, found her favourite sitcom.

But as the titles rolled at the end, she realised she hadn't laughed once. Normally she'd chuckle through every scene. Was it only funny when she was drinking? Feeling cold and fed up, she went to bed early.

Normally she could only face strong black coffee, but today she felt hungry

They'd had a couple of dances, but as the evening wore on, she'd lost sight of him. As it would be her last drink for a month – which felt like forever – she'd been determined to enjoy herself.

"Can we play Azul?" Scarlett asked after supper on January 1. "It's fun. We play it at Dad's."

She didn't really like board games, but when Nate explained the rules, it sounded fairly easy to play.

As they opened the box on the kitchen table, Lexie reached for a glass.

"Remember, Mum, only soft drinks."

Oh yes, she'd almost forgotten. As

But in the morning, she woke to the sun nudging the curtains. Had she slept through the alarm? She checked her phone. No, it hadn't gone off.

Normally she'd press the snooze button twice before getting up, but this morning she didn't need to; she felt fantastic. For the first time in ages, she was truly rested.

After showering, she went through to the kitchen. Normally she could only face strong black coffee, but this morning she felt hungry.

"What are you cooking, Mum?" Nate asked, tying his shoelaces. ➤

"Eggs and bacon. Do you want some?"

"Please!" He pulled out a dining chair.

Lexie enjoyed a noisy breakfast with the children, which made an enjoyable change from the usual weekday blur of toast and hurried coffee as they rushed out of the door.

At work, her old enthusiasm returned.

"You've completed so many tasks today, Lex," Vicky, her line manager, said. "You're making us all look bad. What's got into you?"

"Oh, it's a new year, the sun's shining and it's time to push this business along."

"Great! Keep it up," Vicky smiled.

Later, when they shut down the computers, Vicky asked if she'd like to join her at the pub.

Kindle, the oven sparkled and all her paperwork was neatly filed.

She felt organised and rested. Maybe abstinence had benefits, after all.

And when she next saw Tom, he was incredulous.

"You're joining the gym?"

"Don't look like that – I'm not exactly a couch potato."

"No, but you're not Mo Farah either. What's sparked this?" he asked.

"Ed has the kids on Wednesdays. I felt it was time to get active."

"Well, good for you… I don't recognise you. Have you got a new fella?"

"No, but maybe I'll meet a gym bunny and fall hopelessly in love."

Tom laughed.

Without thinking, she stormed into the kitchen and opened the fridge

For a split second, she longed to accept. Mum collected the children from school and never minded if she was late. Then she remembered – Dry January.

"Er… not tonight. I… must get to Mum's. She's going out."

"Oh, another night then."

"Of course," she smiled, slipping on her coat. "Enjoy Gunwharf."

Driving to Mum's in Elm Grove, she wondered if she'd made the right decision. She got on well with Vicky and could've ordered a soft drink. But a nagging voice asked: could she honestly refuse an alcoholic drink if it was offered?

Waiting at the traffic lights, she wondered for the first time, was she addicted?

Although the evenings stretched out without wine o'clock to look forward to, this proved a bonus.

She started reading the novels on her

"Drink? I've got a lovely Pinot Grigio."

Lexie nearly said yes before telling him, "I'd love a coffee."

Tom's green eyes grew round.

"Now I am worried. Are you ill?"

She laughed.

"It's Dry January. Mum doesn't think I'll do it, but I'm showing her."

"Looks like I'm drinking alone. Slippery slope or what?" He laughed, reaching for the kettle.

For the first time that month, Lexie felt jittery, tempted to join Tom. Would one glass hurt? She could go back to being good tomorrow.

"Sure?" Tom waved the bottle of wine.

She hesitated. It was so difficult to say no. Suddenly, silently, she questioned, why was it difficult?

"No," she said, firmly. "Coffee's great."

Not drinking was a struggle for her, and that wasn't right.

She'd considered herself simply a

sociable drinker, but was it more than that?

The evening with Tom had been fun, but as she drove home, drinking was still on her mind.

Dry January had started as a dare, a kind of New Year's Resolution, but it proved to be her epiphany. Had she been drinking too much?

Did she rely on alcohol for the support she missed from Ed?

These were difficult questions, but at least she was asking them. That was progress, surely.

Monday was horrible. A tenant, Mrs Ellis, phoned to complain about an uncompleted task Lexie had assigned to a workman last week.

"It's not good enough. The boiler keeps turning off. I come home to a cold house and no hot water. And it was minus two last night," Mrs Ellis informed her.

"I understand. I…"

"If you did, you'd get the contractor to repair it. Three times I've called now…"

"I'm sorry, Mrs Ellis. I'll chase up the gas fitter now."

"You said that to me on Friday. And the day before."

It took ages to calm the tenant down and when she phoned Ed, he didn't answer so she left a voicemail.

She was back at the flat by the time Ed texted a reply.

Tenant sorted… I'm booking a holiday. Need dates for the children. End of May?

Lexie groaned. She'd hoped to take the children camping in the New Forest then. She phoned him.

"Sorry Ed, I'm planning to take Scarlett and Nate away that week."

"Since when?"

Why did he always sound grumpy?

"Since I haggled the time off work."

He sighed. "They'll enjoy Spain more."

Lexie rolled her eyes. She tried to reason with him, but the conversation ended badly, and she was shaking when she came off the phone.

Without thinking, she stormed into the kitchen and opened the fridge, automatically reaching for the wine.

"What am I doing?" she said, aloud, putting the bottle on the kitchen table.

She didn't want to ruin her Dry January. It was halfway through the month, and she hadn't broken it yet.

Why did she need a drink so much? Surely she shouldn't reach for alcohol when she was angry, hurt or stressed.

She opened the bottle, but then hesitated. Quickly and decisively, she poured it down the sink.

Over shepherd's pie, dinner was loud and cheerful as Nate and Scarlett shared their school news.

"Oh, Dad called earlier – asked if you'd like to go to Spain in May."

"But aren't we going camping?" Scarlett asked.

"We were, but we thought we'd ask what you'd prefer to do."

Scarlett looked at Nate, then said, "We don't care where we go on holiday, but what we'd like most is to go with you both. Like we used to." ➜

Lexie sighed, then gently pointed out that separated couples didn't go away together, and that they'd have the best of both worlds – time with each parent over two holidays.

"But Sophie and Laura's mum and dad still do stuff together. They had a joint Christmas and New Year. Why can't we?"

"Dad and I don't get on like that."

"But you used to," Nate said, reaching for the brown sauce.

Lexie sat and thought. The children were right. She did used to get on with Ed. Surely they could again.

B it weird – you asking me to Goodies." Ed frowned, a light in his blue eyes. She'd forgotten how blue they were.

"Wow. Bet you're finding that hard."

She was about to lie, but Ed was the father of her children, the man she'd spent twelve years of her life with. She sighed.

"I did. To start with. But as the month passes, it's getting easier.

"And I've found heaps of benefits. I feel better. Brighter. I don't need to drink. I can have fun without it."

"You weren't a heavy drinker, but it did… change things."

She stared into his eyes. It was the first time they'd really talked in ages.

The waitress brought their meals then.

"Changed things?" she asked, cutting into her salmon.

He nodded, grinding pepper over his steak. "Made you sharp. Less easy-going."

She was about to lie, but Ed was the father of her children

"I suppose, but we need a chat. To clear the air." Lexie passed Ed the menu.

When they were together, Goodies had been their restaurant of choice for lunches or can't-be-bothered-to-cook nights.

"Have we air to clear?" he asked.

Lexie took a deep breath.

"Not as such, but things could be… warmer between us. We've the children to consider, and we still work together. And after twelve years, it would be good to salvage something. Friendship, at least."

The waitress came to take their order.

"Wine?" he asked.

"No thanks, water's fine."

He frowned, and gave their food order.

Once the waitress had gone, Ed said, "Actually you're right. It's not good for the children to hear us bickering."

She sipped her water.

"No, and we don't need to."

"So, how come you're not drinking?"

"I'm doing Dry January." She smiled.

She considered his words. Before, she'd have challenged him, argued that it was his behaviour and not her drinking that had spoiled their relationship.

She drank her water. "The children were talking about Spain…"

"They want to go?"

"Yes, but… they want us all to go, together. Of course, I told them that was impossible."

"Actually, that's a good idea."

She stopped eating and looked at him in surprise.

"You agree?"

"Why not? It's a solution and we can take time between now and May to have a few more lunches.

"We can test out our new friendship. Especially if you're no longer drinking."

Ed smiled, reminding her what she'd loved about him.

"You know what? I'll drink to that." She raised her glass of water. Ⓜ

Brain Boosters

Sudoku

					4	1		
		6	4					8
			1		2			6
8	3			6				
	5		4		7	9	3	
	1			5			6	
7								
3			7	9	1			
5	9	6			4			

Fill in each of the blank squares with the numbers 1 to 9, so that each row, each column and each 3x3 cell contains all the numbers from 1 to 9.

Turn To Page 171 For Solutions

Word Wheel

You have ten minutes to find as many words as possible using the letters in the wheel. Each word must be three letters or more and contain the central letter. Use each letter once and no plurals, foreign words or porper nouns are allowed. There is at least one nine-letter word.

Reading The Signs

Was there a spark? Lyndall couldn't be sure… but she realised that she wanted to find out

By **Kathryn England**

Lyndall started jogging when her faithful old stretch jeans didn't stretch far enough any more.

After a recent break-up, she'd sought consolation in food, particularly over Christmas. Her New Year's resolution was to do something about it.

Sticking to a fitness regime was a challenge. It meant getting up earlier each day to jog in the park before driving to the school where she worked as a nursery teacher.

The park was just a short walk from home and she jogged Monday to Saturday, starting later on Saturdays and giving herself Sundays off.

On one of her Saturday runs, Lyndall passed a man on a bench beside the path.

The following Saturday, instead of watching the path wind beneath her trainers, Lyndall looked ahead. The bench was around a bend in the path, hidden from her view by flowering bushes.

As she got closer, she saw a foot crossed over a knee, then the sketch pad came into view. She was a few yards from the bench when the man dropped his pencil. It rolled onto the path and she had to spring over his hand as he retrieved it.

"That was close," she said as she jogged on. Further down the path, she allowed herself a backwards glance and caught the man watching her.

She could usually read the signs – a look in the eye, a gesture, a spark of connection. But this time, perhaps because her heart was still a little raw, she wasn't sure.

She allowed herself a backward glance and caught the man watching her

He was sketching in a pad and happened to look up as she jogged by.

He smiled at her. He wasn't what she would call handsome, but he had a good-natured face.

She'd had enough of handsome. It was looks that had first attracted her to her ex and she'd soon realised it was a shallow start to a relationship.

On her next Saturday jog, she hoped the bench would be occupied, but realised the artist might have moved on.

Seeing him absorbed in his work, she slowed to a walk, then perched at the end of the bench. His body was turned slightly away from her.

"Lovely morning." She winced. She'd never been good at small talk. ➜

IMAGES: SHUTTERSTOCK

He raised the pad and moved it around, viewing his work from different angles. She could see now that the sketch of the park was almost complete.

"You're very talented."

Silence. He was obviously too focused on his creation to be distracted.

She got up and continued her jog, not looking back this time, and resisting the urge to visit the park kiosk for some sweet comfort on the way home.

After breakfast, she went through sample home readers the school had ordered from a new supplier. The headteacher wanted her feedback.

As she went through the colourful little books with their simple words and illustrations, a seed was planted in her mind. By the time she'd finished, the seed had sprouted into a tendril of thought and grown into a possibility.

That day, Lyndall became a student again, learning a new language.

On the following Saturday run, she slowed down as she approached the bend in the path.

The artist had almost finished his sketch the week before. He might have moved on to another source of inspiration.

fingers then signed, "My name is Lyndall."

The man's expression said more than whatever words he signed back.

Having already reached her sign language limit, Lyndall produced a pad and pen from her pocket. She learned his name was Brian. Passing the pad back and forth, the conversation continued.

The seed had sprouted into a tendril of thought and grown into a possibility

A little further along the path, she let out the breath she'd been unconsciously holding. He was there. His eyes were closed as if he were deep in thought.

She sat at the end of the bench again. This day, the pad was open at a new page – a sketch of a jogger.

"Hello." Lyndall was not really surprised when there was no response.

She gently touched the man's shoulder and waved a hand, the sign for hello. Her

It ended with a dinner invitation, which the artist accepted.

Eighteen months later, when the celebrant asked Lyndall a question using both words and signs to accommodate all the wedding guests, Lyndall pointed proudly to herself.

She then formed a D with fingers of both hands and touched the fourth fingertip of her left hand with the tip of her right forefinger to form the letter O. Ⓜ

Brain Boosters

Codeword

Each letter of the alphabet has been replaced by a number. The numbers for the first name of our pictured celebrity are given. Work out which number represents which letter in the grid to reveal in which US drama Nicole Kidman played Celeste Wright.

17	8	25	13	24	14	6	22	5	8	22		11	13	3
13		6		6		2		8		8		22		8
16	6	11	11	21		16	26	12	4	25	24	8	16	16
6		26		13		25			13		23		2
1	26	23	6	24	8		10	2	3	26	23	26	13	24
N		**I**	**C**	**O**	**L**	**E**								
		13						1		16		25
2	1	24	26	25					18	8	22	6
1											22
8	19	8	22					15	2	16	16	21
13		1		11					2		
22	8	23	5	6	1	8	3		1	8	13	22	20	21
25		22		25			6		7		11		26
4	13	21	17	13	5	26	1	12		2	16	13	12	8
24		11		25		23		24		26		16		24
21	8	25		6	19	8	22	8	9	11	6	16	8	3

A B C̸ D E̸ F G H I̸ J K L̸ M N̸ O̸ P Q R S T U V W X Y Z

1	2	3	4	5	6	7	8	9	10	11	12	13
N					**O**		**E**					
14	15	16	17	18	19	20	21	22	23	24	25	26
									C	**L**		**I**

Turn To Page 171 For Solutions

| 20 | 26 | 12 | | 24 | 26 | 25 | 25 | 24 | 8 | | 24 | 26 | 8 | 16 |
| | **I** | | | **L** | **I** | | | **L** | **E** | | **L** | **I** | **E** | |

Lamb Tagine

Ingredients (Serves 2)

- 1tbsp sunflower oil
- 1 onion, chopped
- 300g lean lamb leg, cut into chunks
- 1 garlic clove, chopped
- 2.5cm piece fresh root ginger, grated
- 2tsp ras el hanout spice mix
- 400g can chopped tomatoes
- 200ml vegetable stock
- 400g can chickpeas, drained
- 75g dried apricots
- 175g couscous
- Salt and freshly ground black pepper
- Few fresh coriander and mint leaves, to garnish

1 Preheat the oven to 190°C, fan 170°C, Gas 5. Heat oil in a flameproof casserole dish, add the onion and sauté for 5 minutes. Add the lamb and cook for 5 minutes, until browned.

2 Add the garlic, ginger and ras el hanout. Stir to combine and cook for 1 minute. Stir in the tomatoes, stock, chickpeas and apricots. Season well and cover. Transfer to the oven and cook for 45min.

3 Place the couscous in a bowl and add 200ml boiling water. Cover and leave to stand for 5 minutes. Fluff up with a fork and divide between two plates or bowls. Top with the lamb and garnish with coriander and mint leaves.

Twin Souls

Fate seemed to be pulling them together. So why did Liza keep pushing her new neighbour away?

By Carrie Hewlett

Liza smiled as she pulled into the drive of Gossamer Cottage. Grey castle stone, a roof of fine tile and cottage pane windows. Just like its neighbour.

In fact, they looked like twins with only a brick wall separating the small but well-tended front gardens. There was a sprinkling of other houses nearby with rolling hills surrounding them on all sides.

She'd rented the cottage for six months while she looked for somewhere to buy, having got a new job in a large advertising firm. And she'd been glad to move.

Her previous landlord had hated the idea of pets, so she'd never even been able to get a goldfish.

He'd also been a bit of a creep, continually badgering her for a date despite her telling him she wasn't interested. She blew out her cheeks in frustration. Why did some men do that?

As she got out of her car, she heard a screech of brakes. Fearing a nasty accident, she rushed towards the road, but all she saw was a red van and a ginger tom nonchalantly washing its face with its paw on the pavement opposite.

The man behind the wheel got out and dragged a hand through his hair as if in despair. He seemed upset and frowned as he shouted at the cat.

"You may have nine lives, but I think they're nearly up! Next time you might not be so lucky."

"Hey," Liza exclaimed. "Thankfully he's OK, so no harm done."

The man looked at her, his lips pressed firmly together.

"It could have been killed. I shall have words with its owner."

Despite only being five foot two, Liza squared her shoulders as she looked up at him. The man really did seem enormous, – well over six foot. A sort of Jack Reacher type with dark brown hair woven with strands of gold, and green eyes the colour of new spring growth.

But even though he was good-looking, he seemed to have zero personality.

"Cats own people, not the other way. And all it was doing was crossing the road," she countered.

The man harrumphed and threw up his hands, before getting back into the van and driving off.

All she saw was a red van and a ginger tom nonchalantly washing its face

Liza rolled her eyes. Men! She glanced back at the cat who stared at her quizzically before stalking down the street, its tail held high in the air as though it didn't have a care in the world.

Her lips twitched. Cats were amazing; independent and sometimes aloof, but still very lovable. She glanced back at the cottage. OK. First things first. Get settled in and then go shopping for food.

The man she'd communicated with ➡

via email said he lived next door and was a landscape gardener. That showed in the well-kept front gardens.

He'd been most helpful, sending photos of the cottage as well as information on the surrounding area which looked idyllic.

She couldn't wait to explore.

Opening the front door, she admired the nicely furnished interior.

She glanced at the calendar on the wall, a circle around January 14 – today. Maybe a reminder of her arrival.

Idly she flicked the page to the

Well, he would have been had he not been scowling. Why had he looked so upset?

Thankfully he'd not hit the cat. Yes, it was annoying, but surely there'd been no need to act so irrationally.

She was just glad the cat was OK.

Arriving back, she saw the same man standing by the recycling bins in the front garden of the cottage next door, the red van in the drive.

"Hi." He gave her a friendly smile, his face transformed from earlier.

His voice ended on a questioning note, a look of hope on his face

next month, noting an asterisk next to February 14. Valentine's Day.

Huh. Romance was for books, not real life. At least, not for her – as she was disastrous at relationships, or so her last boyfriend had told her sourly when they'd broken up after two months.

She gave a wry grin, remembering what her gran had said.

"You've just not met the right one yet, my girl. One day, your eyes will meet and that will be it.

"It's how I met your grandfather. I'd gone to a Valentine's disco with some friends, and this rather geeky man asked me to dance."

Her grandmother's eyes had misted.

"As soon as he held me in his arms and I gazed into his soft brown eyes, I knew he was the one. We were like twin souls meant to be together."

Liza sighed. So romantic. If only it could be like that for her.

Driving down to the shops for food, her mind returned to the man from earlier. He had a Herculean physique and was handsome in a rakish kind of way.

"I take it you're Liza Nightshade?"

"Yes." How did he know her name?

Her face coloured slightly for some annoying reason. After his earlier behaviour, she was not going to be taken in by a charming smile.

"I'm Chris Lennox. We've been emailing about the cottage. You're renting it from me for six months."

"Ohhh. Yes." Realisation dawned. But the man she'd been emailing had seemed so friendly and open.

He ran a hand through his dark hair sheepishly, as he looked at her with a shamefaced expression.

"And apologies for earlier. I… um… might have overreacted over the cat. But I was rushing to another job and was running late."

He sighed, and his gaze clouded.

"I had to take my own cat to the vets a few days ago after she'd been hit by a car. Sadly, her outcome wasn't so lucky and it really upset me.

"I suppose I was trying, in my own silly way, to warn Mrs Smith's cat not to take chances like that. But Simba, like all cats, does what she wants."

Liza gave him a sympathetic look.

"I'm sorry to hear that."

Chris shrugged, though his face darkened once more.

"What upset me the most was the fact that whoever knocked Marcie over left her by the edge of the road."

"That's terrible!"

Chris nodded, his face pained, before he made an effort to smile.

"Perhaps as way of apology, I could show you around the area?"

His voice ended on a questioning note, a look of hope on his face.

Liza stubbornly shook her head.

OK, he was nice. But his behaviour earlier showed he could be erratic.

"No, it's fine. I'm sure I'll discover it on my own when I have time."

"Oh… OK." His face fell and Liza could hear slight surprise and perhaps a degree of disappointment in his voice.

Well, tough! She wasn't about to fall for a winning smile.

"Bye, then." She turned on her heel and went inside.

As the weeks flew past, she found herself thinking of Chris more and more. Her new job kept her busy and it wasn't until early February that she happened to see Chris Lennox standing in a nearby garden, spade in hand.

His sleeves were rolled up and his muscles strained against the fabric.

Almost mesmerised, she watched him expertly digging up a shrub.

"He's fit, isn't he?"

A female voice to Liza's left interrupted her reverie.

"What? Oh. I guess," Liza said offhandedly, ignoring her racing pulse as she turned to face a woman of about her own age.

"I'd be interested if I wasn't already married." The woman chuckled. "Plenty of others are too, but I think he's still single. He inherited the cottages after his parents passed away."

"Oh, I didn't realise. I'm renting one of them. Did his parents own both?"

The woman nodded. "Yes. But they rented one out like him. So sad, losing ➜

both of them in such quick succession."

Liza nodded, feeling a wave of compassion for Chris. And then losing his cat. No wonder he'd been upset.

The woman glanced at her watch before giving another friendly smile. "Enjoy your stay."

"Thanks." Continuing on her way, Liza mulled over what she'd been told. Perhaps she should be a bit more friendly, considering what he'd been through.

about to land in the cold water, she was startled to feel strong arms around her waist, steadying her.

"I've got you. Are you OK?"

Liza turned her head to see Chris's concerned face.

"I would have been if you hadn't made me lose my balance!"

Chris looked abashed.

"I'm sorry. I was just going to warn you that those rocks can get slippery."

Liza fell to her knees at the irresistible sight of the small, mewing cats

Waiting in the queue at the post office, her gaze fell on a card on the cork board.

Kittens for Sale. Please contact Lion Farm for details.

There was a telephone number which Liza jotted into the notes section of her phone. Maybe she'd ask Chris if it would be alright first? Just to be polite.

A few days later and feeling the need for some fresh air, she decided to go for a walk.

Though they'd had rain, the puddles remained free of ice and there were green shoots rising cautiously from the earth as if to check whether it was spring yet.

Wending her way along a path not far from the cottages, she followed the sound of trickling water, smiling as she saw a wooden bridge straddling a stream.

There were large flat stepping stones which brought back memories from her childhood when she and her brothers would compete to see who could cross first without falling in.

She stepped on one, then another and was about to leap to a third when a male voice called out, making her jump. She wobbled, losing her balance.

Feeling herself slip and fearing she was

Liza gave him a hard stare.

"I'm wearing good trainers and I would have been fine."

Chris held up his hands in a defensive fashion. "OK. Sorry, again. I was just trying to help."

"Well, don't!" Liza tempered her tone and explained.

"I used to play in those woods when I was growing up. There was a small brook there, too. We used to skim stones or play Pooh sticks."

Chris smiled. "Me too." He waved a hand at the bridge, his eyes twinkling. "Fancy a go now?"

Liza found herself smiling back. "Sure."

As they tossed sticks into the river on the upstream of the bridge, then went to the other side to see which stick appeared downstream first, they chatted.

Liza discovered that after his parents passed away, Chris decided he wanted to move back into the family home as it held so many happy memories.

As he talked, Liza found herself warming to him. Not only was he attractive, but he was funny, kind and sensitive. Maybe his earlier outburst at Simba the cat was a one-off.

She tentatively raised the subject of a pet. "I was thinking of getting a kitten, if that's OK? The lease does say animals are allowed. And there was a notice in the post office from Lion Farm.

"But with you losing Marcie recently…" Her voice faded as she saw his forehead crease. But then he smiled.

"That's fine. If you like, I can drive you there. Mrs Giles was a friend of my mother's. They're a lovely family. It would be nice to see them again."

"Great."

"When would you like to go?"

"Tomorrow?"

"Would ten-thirty be OK? It's just that I've got a job on tomorrow afternoon."

Liza nodded, aware of a warmth flooding her at the thought of spending more time with him.

The journey wasn't long. When they got there, Mrs Giles gave Chris a hug.

"You should visit more often," she said. "The kittens are in the barn. This way."

Liza fell to her knees at the irresistible sight of the small, mewing cats.

"They're gorgeous!"

Chris had a strange expression on his face as he looked at her.

"Yes. Gorgeous."

Self-consciously, Liza pushed a strand of blonde hair behind one ear. The air felt electric. ➜

"We're keeping the tabby, but the other two are up for grabs," Mrs Giles said. "We did have six kittens, but the other three have found good homes. They're nine weeks old now, so weaned, and have had their first vaccinations."

Liza picked up the black and white kitten that seemed to be falling over its feet as it moved around.

Mrs Giles smiled. "Still a bit accident-prone, that one, but she'll be fine."

Liza stroked the kitten's soft fur, before glancing over to see Chris enamoured with a white and tabby kitten.

When he picked it up, it almost looked lost in his large hands, but was obviously very much at home and licked his thumb.

"Has she been named yet?" he asked.

Valentine's Day next Wednesday I'd love to take you out for a coffee. The coffee shop does the most delicious cakes and pastries."

He looked at her hopefully and Liza felt her heart melt. Yes. They had got off on the wrong foot several times. But they were here now. And she liked him. Her heart dipped and she felt her cheeks flush.

"I'd like that. By the way, what are you going to call your kitten?"

Chris gave a sheepish grin.

"If I tell you, you'll probably never speak to me again."

"OK, you've got to tell me now. I promise our date is still on."

Chris took a deep breath.

They had got off on the wrong foot several times. But they were here now

"No. But she's a right independent little miss. More so than the others. Maybe that's why she wasn't the first to go."

"I'm happy to take her."

Mrs Giles beamed. "Perfect."

Reaching what Liza now thought of as home, Chris gave her a shy smile.

"Thanks."

"For what?"

"For letting me take you out to Lion Farm. I probably wouldn't have taken the first step towards getting another cat so quickly, but as soon as I saw them, I couldn't help myself."

Liza smiled back.

"Animals bring love into our lives and while cats are more independent than dogs, they still seem to know when you need a cuddle."

"They do. Um… this is probably going to come out wrong as we seem to keep getting off on the wrong foot, but with

"Pipsqueak. It's just that when I first met you, you were laying into me and it annoyed me. But then I couldn't get you out of my head. And in living next door, we kept seeing each other. And well…" He spread his hands.

Liza grinned, seeing the funny side. "Pipsqueak could grow into a feisty cat!" she teased.

He laughed. "I like feisty! So, what are you going to call your kitten?"

"Valentine," she said softly. "Just because…"

Chris gave a small smile. "Perfect."

Though their romance hadn't been as immediate as her grandparents' had been, Liza had a feeling that the attraction between her and Chris had.

Maybe their twin souls had just needed a bit of time to ignite. Either way, Liza knew that putting her roots down in the cottage had been one of the best moves she had made, ever. **MW**

Mac, Leek And Cheese

Ingredients (serves 2-3)

- ◆ **125g macaroni**
- ◆ **25g butter**
- ◆ **1 leek, chopped**
- ◆ **1 garlic clove, crushed**
- ◆ **25g plain flour**
- ◆ **400ml milk**
- ◆ **75g mature cheddar cheese, grated**
- ◆ **1tsp English mustard**
- ◆ **2tbsp fresh breadcrumbs**
- ◆ **Salt and freshly ground black pepper**
- ◆ **Thyme leaves, to garnish, optional**
- ◆ **Tomato, onion and basil salad, to serve (optional)**

1 Preheat the oven to 200°C, fan 180°C, Gas 6. Place the macaroni in a saucepan of boiling, lightly salted water and cook for 8 minutes. Drain.

2 Meanwhile melt the butter, add the leek and cook for 4-5 minutes to soften. Stir in the garlic and flour and then gradually stir in the milk. Bring to the boil, stirring constantly until thickened. Stir in ¾ of the cheese, along with the mustard and the macaroni. Season to taste.

3 Transfer to a 1-litre ovenproof dish, sprinkle with the breadcrumbs and remaining cheese and bake for 25 minutes, until golden. Cook in individual dishes for 20 minutes, if preferred. Garnish with thyme leaves and serve with a tomato, onion and basil salad, if wished.

RECIPE AND FOOD STYLING: JENNIE SHAPTER PHOTOGRAPHY: JON WHITAKER

Too Much Imagination

Amid the Big Freeze of 1963, observant Edith has a
great deal of cynicism to contend with…

By Beth Francis

Borrowers at the library where Edith worked said it was the coldest winter they could remember. She was relieved when the last person left and they could lock up. Eight o'clock and the streets were already deserted. She hated the walk to the bus stop on these dark winter nights.

Already uneasy, she tensed when she sensed someone behind her and screamed as a hand grabbed her shoulder.

Not realising it was her boyfriend, Patrick, she swung at him with her bag full

of books, slipped on the ice and fell over.

Patrick thought it side-splittingly funny.

"Those books could do some serious damage," he spluttered, helping her up.

"That's the point!" she yelled. "I thought you were attacking me."

"Who's going to attack you?"

They quarrelled all the way home.

"She's got too much imagination," Patrick told her parents.

"She reads too many books. I keep telling her," her father said.

"Better she reads them than hits people with them," Patrick said.

Her father thought that was hilarious.

Edith didn't like being laughed at. She didn't like being talked about as if she wasn't there, either.

Patrick chuckled on and off all evening.

"Nearly brained me with that bag, you did," he kept repeating.

"It's a pity I didn't," she muttered.

The next morning, the home service weather report was threatening yet more snowfall across the country.

Edith left the warmth of the bus and walked along the icy pavements towards the library, pulling her scarf close around her face as the freezing air set her teeth aching. She finished work at five today. Hopefully the buses would still be running.

Outside every shop along the street, people were busy clearing the frontages, chatting as they worked.

"Never known weather like it."

"Pipes burst in our kitchen."

She nodded and smiled, but was ➤

preoccupied, remembering last night's argument with Patrick. She wouldn't be seeing him again.

Mr Telford was spreading cinders on the pavement outside his newsagents.

"You're early today, Edith."

"It's Bert's day off. I need to clear the snow from the library steps before we open," she explained. "Shall I take the newspapers up for you?"

"They've gone already. I sent Robert with them."

She met Rob on his way back.

"Want a hand with your bag? It looks pretty heavy," he said.

"I can manage perfectly well. It's only a few books," she snapped.

He shrugged and turned to go.

Edith sighed. She hadn't meant to be sharp. She liked Rob. She'd been at school with him. It was Patrick who she was annoyed with.

"Sorry, Rob," she called after him.

A shovel was propped by the library door beside a bag of rock salt. Edith called hello, dumped her bag and set to work, shovelling the fresh snow away, clearing the ice, then spreading salt on the steps.

"Take the brush and shovel down to the cellar and throw a few shovels of fuel into the boiler while you're there," Miss Prosser the librarian said when Edith eventually went in. "Then go and have a mug of tea to warm up. I'll help Elaine deal with the early borrowers."

Bert kept the ancient boiler working, tending it with loving care, but on his day off they needed to add fuel themselves.

The cellar was his domain. It was gloomy, narrow and claustrophobic.

"Remember to close the door after you," Miss Prosser said. "We don't want dust getting into the library."

Edith was rather afraid that the door would jam and shut her in, but she didn't complain. She was on probation and she really wanted this job.

A dim bulb lit the stairs and the front of the boiler. She propped the brush in a corner and opened the furnace door.

The fire blazed as she threw in several shovel loads of fuel. Once the boiler was fed and the heavy door closed, the cellar returned to gloom.

Weak daylight filtered through the grid, set into the pavement, through which fuel was delivered every week.

Footsteps were coming and going.

"Like the start of *A Tale of Two Cities*," she muttered. "Maybe Dad's right. I do read too many books."

She turned to go, but her hand brushed against a huge spider's web. She didn't mind spiders. It was fear of being trapped in small, dark places that scared her.

As she watched the spider scurry away, people stopped on the pavement above and blocked the daylight. The smell of cigarette smoke drifted down, followed by a spent matchstick being dropped through the grid.

She heard a woman's voice.

"Time to move on."

"Not yet." A man's voice this time.

"We need to keep ahead of the police."

"No one suspects us. That old dear yesterday even gave us a cup of tea and thanked us for being so kind."

"We've stayed too long already."

The man's accent was definitely local, but not the woman's.

Black Country? No, Liverpudlian.

"We can't stay in your grandfather's derelict cottage much longer. There's no electric or water. The pipes are frozen. They'll burst once the thaw sets in."

"We'll leave soon, then you can have all the hot water you want."

"Unless I freeze first."

A cigarette butt fell through the grating.

"Come on. We've got work to do."

returned books were piling up on the trolleys. Everyone was coming to change their books in case they were snowed in.

The reading room was full of people looking at newspapers or pretending to study telephone directories or stamp catalogues while keeping warm. Edith saw a pair of socks drying on the radiator. She pretended not to notice.

As she walked to the bus stop after work, she thought again about reporting what she had overheard.

In her imagination, the policeman laughed at her.

"Been reading too many lurid crime stories, have we?"

She could almost hear his scoffing voice – a lot like her father's, or Patrick's.

"Forget it. You probably misheard. Go and have a mug of tea"

The couple moved on down the street.

Edith had work to do, too. She hurried up the steps to the ordered peace and quiet of the library.

Elaine was busy at the desk. Miss Prosser was talking to a borrower. Everything as normal. She could almost have imagined the last few minutes.

"When I was down in the cellar, I overheard a couple outside talking about conning old people out of money," she whispered to Elaine.

"Really?" Elaine raised her eyebrows, but continued to discharge a pile of books.

"Should I tell the police?"

"Would you recognise them?"

"I didn't see them. But I think I'd know their voices."

"Forget it. You probably misheard. Go and have a mug of tea, then come back and sort out the newspapers."

When Edith returned to the library, there were queues at the desk and

Rob was waiting in the queue. Snow was falling heavily.

"I hope the buses are still running when I finish at night school," he said.

She was tempted to confide in him, knowing he wouldn't laugh, but the bus came and the moment passed.

The smell of beef stew and cabbage greeted her as she arrived home. They sat round the kitchen table, Edith only half listening as her parents chatted.

"People aren't clearing their pavements properly," her mother said. "I nearly slipped going to the shop."

"*Worst winter on record. Colder than 1949*," her father read out from the evening paper.

"Good thing I got extra coal in over the summer," her mother commented.

"Disgusting. Crooks have been conning pensioners. Taking money to do work then disappearing, or buying their ➤

valuable antiques for just a few quid."

Edith was listening now.

"I overheard two people talking about cheating old people when I was at work today," she said.

"I've heard it all now." Her father laughed. "Where were they? Don't tell me. In the crime section?"

"They weren't in the library. They were standing on the pavement outside. I was down in the cellar and heard them through the grating."

"What exactly do you think you heard?" her mother asked.

Edith told them. It didn't sound much.

"Better get straight down the police station," her father scoffed. "They'll be able to make instant arrests."

"On a golden beach with nothing to worry about except not getting sunburned." Edith sighed.

"What's worrying you, Edith? Had a row with Patrick?"

"I've finished with Patrick. It's something else bothering me."

She told him what she'd heard.

Rob didn't laugh, scoff or tell her she had too much imagination. He listened.

"They must be staying somewhere nearby. We need more information, but I don't see how we can get it," he said.

The bus was overcrowded. Edith found a seat just inside, but Rob had to stand.

"Move on down the bus, now, please," the conductor called out as he began to collect their fares.

The woman had disappeared, but her footprints were clear in the snow

"Even if it was them, you didn't hear enough to be any use. What time's Patrick coming?" her mother said.

"He's not. I've finished with him."

"Really? Why?" Her father finally put down the newspaper.

"I got fed up with him ganging up with you to make fun of me."

"No sense of humour, that's your trouble. No sense of humour – and too much imagination."

The library was busy throughout the next day, but as she worked Edith was still fretting about what she had overheard. As she passed the newsagents on her way home, she saw Rob. They walked to the bus stop together.

"Do you think I've got too much imagination?" she asked him.

"Can you have too much imagination? I'm imagining I'm in the Mediterranean right now," he said with a grin.

Edith was feeling less troubled. Rob believed her. Might he come to the police station with her?

Her calmer mood was shattered as the woman in the seat in front of her asked the conductor for a ticket to the Golden Lion. She'd know that voice anywhere. She'd last heard it when she was in the library cellar.

Edith tried to see the woman's face, but she was so wrapped up against the cold it was impossible.

Rob was standing near the front of the bus, and she couldn't get his attention.

Determined not to let the thief get away, she followed her when the bus halted at the Golden Lion.

Edith knew this stop well. There was a police station a few hundred yards away. She could walk in, tell them what she knew and pass the responsibility to them.

Undecided, she watched the woman turn into the lane that led to a few derelict cottages and the allotments. It might be her only chance to get more information.

She followed, her feet crunching on the icy track, sounding loud in the frosty air. She moved to the left to walk on the softer snow lying on the verge.

The woman had disappeared, but her footprints were clear in the snow by the gate into the allotments.

A van was parked nearby. Edith memorised the number plate as she sidled through the gate. She saw the woman talking to a man a few plots away before they both went into a nearby shed.

She shrank against the hedge, edging along until she could hear their voices, then crept to the back of the shed.

"You took your time. What kept you?"

"The old dear had the cash, but insisted I had a cup of tea and a slice of Victoria sponge before I left."

"You should have just grabbed the money and run."

"We're supposed to be charming them, remember? Don't want her suspicious. She'd recognise me. We need to get out of here before the roads become impassable."

"Calm down. I've finished loading the van. Grandad's shed has been great to store things. We're ready to leave."

Edith tried to move back towards the hedge as the shed door opened, but slipped and fell. She lay on the ground, trying not to groan.

"Hey, you! What are you doing skulking around?" the man yelled.

Edith was desperately searching for an excuse for being at the allotments when she heard Rob's voice.

"Fetching veg for my grandmother."

He must have seen her leave the bus and followed her.

Fetching vegetables! In this weather! Was that the best he could think of?

She would have laughed if she hadn't been so frightened.

"Nan wants a cabbage. I forgot to come up here earlier."

The man grabbed Rob, pushed him into the shed and locked the door.

"Let's go. Now."

Ignoring Rob's shouts, the crooks hurried towards the van.

Edith hobbled to the shed as soon as they were out of sight.

"I'm here, Rob," she called.

"I know. I let them see me so you didn't get caught. Have they gone?"

"Yes. We need to get over to the police station and report them."

"Is the key in the lock?"

"No, it isn't. We'll have to break the door down, I think."

Rob pounded at the shed door, but it didn't budge.

"I'll smash the window and climb out," he said. "Start running. I'll catch you up."

"I can't run. I've twisted my ankle."

Rob broke the window pane with a wooden stake, then passed it out to her.

"Lean on this and start walking."

As she hobbled along the path, she heard Rob hammering at the window frame until it fell out and crashed onto the ground. Minutes later, he'd climbed out and was running to catch her up. ➜

"You go on ahead," she said, wincing.

"We'll go together. You're the one with the information. Lean on me."

Snow was falling so heavily, the tracks from the van were almost covered. They struggled to keep their footing on the treacherous ground.

By the time they reached the police station, Edith was exhausted.

Rob held the heavy door open as she stumbled into the foyer and limped up to the desk.

"I've just seen the crooks who have been conning people out of their savings," she informed him breathlessly.

"You and half the city." The duty officer sighed and rolled his eyes.

he declared as the mugs of hot tea were brought in.

Edith wrapped her hands round the warm mug. She was shivering, and her ankle was very painful.

"Shouldn't you be at college?" she asked Rob anxiously.

"Too late now. I'll have to miss it."

"My parents will be cross because I'm late. Come with me, Rob, and help me explain what happened."

"They should be proud of you, young lady," the police officer said.

"They won't believe me. They'll say I've got too much imagination."

"They'll believe you when we take you home in a police car and tell them how helpful you've been."

"The neighbours will be wondering why you came home in a police car"

"If you knew how many hysterical women we've had here, all saying they know who it is…"

"I'm not hysterical. I have a description, the number of their van, and I know the man's grandfather owned a shed on the allotments round the corner. They've been hiding stolen goods in it."

The officer's attitude changed.

"Come through to the office. You too, lad. Smith, come and watch the desk for ten minutes. And bring three mugs of tea."

When they sat down, he began to ask questions and make notes.

"They'll be getting away," Edith remarked anxiously.

"Oh, they won't get far. Most of the roads are impassable. We'll catch them. Thanks to you."

He reached for the phone. Edith waited as he gave instructions. He replaced the receiver and beamed at her.

"These two deserve biscuits with that,"

They were driven home through what had become a blizzard.

"We'll let you know as soon as we have information, Edith," the policeman said after he'd talked to her parents. "I'm sure we'll have made arrests before the morning. Now lad, we'll drop you home on our way back to the station."

"Thanks, Rob," Edith said gratefully.

"We made a good team," he said. "See you tomorrow?"

"See you tomorrow." She smiled.

"The neighbours will be wondering why you came home in a police car," her mother said. "I could see curtains twitching as they drove away."

"They'll find out soon enough," her father said. "This will be in all the newspapers in a day or two. You'll be a heroine, Edith."

For a brief moment Edith thought her father was proud of her, but it was probably just her imagination. ⓂⓌ

Brain Boosters

Kriss Kross

Try to fit all of the listed words back into the grid.

4 letters
CURL
SASH

5 letters
ALLOT
METAL
TATTY

7 letters
PRATTLE
TERRACE

8 letters
DREADFUL
MARRIAGE

9 letters
AESTHETIC
REMINISCE

10 letters
PICCALILLI
TITIVATION

11 letters
HAEMOGLOBIN
LATITUDINAL
PREDICTABLE

Turn To
Page 171 For
Solutions

The Golden Notebook

I'd loved my grandma, yet it was only through her writing that I truly came to know and be inspired by her…

By Gabe Ellis

An award-winning gymnast? Grandma Bubs – really?

Sitting on a vinyl-padded chair in the crematorium, the anecdotes I heard were painting a portrait of a woman who had won a place in grammar school, competed in national gymnastics competitions and even had a career. All before bringing up eight children.

I'd assumed that this elderly woman was endlessly curious about my studies, my journalism and my love life because she'd led such a sheltered existence.

Instead, I was hearing about a vibrant, colourful woman who had once been as young as me, with dreams, visions, hopes and ambitions. I regretted not knowing her better. But that was about to change.

"Oh, I've got something for you in the back room," said Mum. "Grandma left you her notebooks."

"Notebooks?"

"Journals and diaries. She was always interested in your writing, probably because she was forever scribbling herself." Mum handed me the bowl of roast potatoes so I could help myself.

"Uncle Harry said that she could well have been a writer herself if times had been different." ➜

"She must have been good, then," I remarked. Great Uncle Harry rarely had a compliment for his sister.

I'd decided to escape the city for the weekend and console myself with Mum's Sunday roast mostly because Rob and I were bickering endlessly.

He hadn't come with me to Grandma's funeral and after two years of living together, I wondered if our university romance was coming to its end.

Besides, I reasoned, Mum could do with a bit of company in the weeks after Grandma's death.

We spent the afternoon sorting through Grandma's ornaments and photos, and I listened to Mum telling me the stories that went with the objects, like a movie reel of her life. Many of the tales were well-worn with telling, others were new to me, providing fresh glimpses into my grandma's character as well as my mum's childhood.

"Oh, the wishbook! I never knew she'd kept this!" Mum exclaimed, cradling a slim notebook with a faded gold cover, stroking it fondly. "When Aunty Pat and I were youngsters, your grandma would sometimes fetch this book if we were desperately upset or worried.

"It was a real honour when she let us write in it, but we had to choose our words carefully, be very clear about our problem and about what solution we hoped for. You know I've said that to you often enough – well, this is where it came from! 'Never underestimate the power of writing or the power of prayer' was one of her sayings.

"But this one is completely blank… how strange. She must have had a stack of these books, of course, bless her!"

Finally, we'd sorted everything into keepsakes for Mum, items for me and charity donations.

My pile included Grandma's journals, the gold notebook and a framed photograph from when she and Grandpa first met, on the back of which I'd found the sentimental inscription *Our courting days in Stratford*. They were both beaming, looking as if they were on a great adventure, which I suppose it is when you first fall in love.

That evening, I was doing some preliminary research for a magazine article about contemporary feminism, but became distracted by Grandma's journals.

Rob came home from the gym to find me cross-legged, surrounded by papers and photos, reading entries from when she finished grammar school and embarked on her first job as secretary on a local newspaper.

I knew this was where she'd met my grandfather, which made me feel I was part of the story.

Her insights into the work and her colleagues were compelling. It felt like looking into a mirror, reading about her at the same stage of life as me: newly qualified and establishing herself professionally in her twenties.

The descriptions of physical, typewritten articles plastered onto large-format boards were foreign to me, but I was caught up in her vivid accounts of last-minute changes when a new story hit just before the press deadline, and she would have to urgently type a new piece as it was dictated, or hammer out shorter versions of edited articles to be literally pasted onto the boards.

Technology has evolved, but the adrenaline of deadlines never changes.

The time flew by as I read page after page of her diaries, and I told myself it was part of my research about feminism.

When Rob came home and observed, "Oh, haven't you sorted anything for dinner?" the comment was not lost on me, but I pointed him towards the kitchen and suggested he rectify the situation.

Later, I showed Rob the photos.

unprofessional conduct, but she just nodded and continued.

"That's just it," she said between mouthfuls. "Our quest for equality means that we can now have jobs, but we still do everything we used to. I can't believe that's what the Suffragettes had in mind."

"We do rather seem to have shot ourselves in the foot, don't we?" I agreed, thinking of Rob's habit of leaving all the washing and food shopping to me, even though I worked longer hours.

"Maybe we should include those other statistics you found, showing that while the blokes in our lives are at the gym or out with their mates, we're cleaning or visiting relatives," said Janice, picking up my notes again and sighing.

Technology has evolved, but the adrenaline of deadlines never changes

He snorted at the phrase "courting" and when I read a couple of paragraphs from the diaries, he said, "Some bird working on a newspaper fifty years ago doesn't really do much for me. Can we put a film on?"

Good job he's not writing about contemporary feminism.

I'd finished my initial research in time for my lunch meeting with my features editor, Janice, and we discussed how to present the statistics in a new way to keep it relevant for our readers.

These professional lunches were still new to me, and rare enough to make me highly nervous.

"So, Cathy, you're doing your hours as a junior staff writer and freelancing in your own time, is that it?"

"Well, yes, I –"

I was terrified that Janice would accuse me of conflicting interests or

"Thank heavens, at least women your age know better, don't they?"

I gulped and scooped up my last forkful of lasagne.

"Right, content's good, but I need you to find a fresh angle on this. It needs to feel personal, more alive. Get a couple of talking heads in there. Two thousand words plus interviews by Friday week. You OK sorting photos with Charlie?"

So, I hurried home and sat down at the kitchen bench, fully intending to brainstorm new angles, but found myself reaching for the journals where I'd dumped them the night before.

No one knows that we've been stepping out, but H is a wonderful man and so talented, I know we could make a great team. He's even asked me to marry him, but he knows I can't contemplate marriage while Father is unwell.

I smiled at that, imagining my Grandpa Hugh proposing so impatiently.

➡

Wonderful news! H has been offered the post of deputy editor for one of the national dailies. It's such a glorious opportunity, I am so proud of him. He says that I inspire him and it's true that his work is filled with ideas that we've discussed together.

I told H I wished I'd been a journalist instead of a secretary, but he patted my cheek and called me fanciful.

I had to remind myself that this was many decades ago, a time when women could never entertain the idea of writing as freely as I did for a living. I'd known that Grandpa Hugh was a newspaper man, but never knew he worked in London.

Did he return for love?

H has settled in rooms in the city.

the engagement of deputy editor Henry Tillerman to society heiress Millicent Wollam. I was shaking with shock and, I shall admit it, the heat of shame.

How could I have thought he loved me? He clearly proposed knowing that I could not accept immediately. Oh, I detest his ambition. I detest my own. I was blinded by the notion of finding my own employment in London and building my own reputation. What arrogant pride!

I am so very angry. I am deceived in H, in myself, and in society. I know that I need to compose myself and be clear in my thoughts. It appears that H did not deserve me, and I certainly deserve better than H.

I was gobsmacked.

I felt as if my genetic heritage was waiting in the wings of her journal

I miss him dreadfully, but am flattered to see that our piece was the lead story in the Friday edition. Seeing his name in bold in the by-line makes my heart swell with pride. H promises to visit and to set a date for our wedding so that we can live in London together.

I might even be able to work in my own right – they are more forward-thinking in the capital.

There followed many similar entries, and I began to get annoyed with Grandpa Hugh for making her wait so long.

Reading between the lines, he was having a whale of a time and leaving her behind. I picked up the photo of Grandma courting and admonished her, but felt compelled to find out how Grandpa came back to Stratford.

I am so very foolish. I feel so ashamed. Thank heavens no one else knew of our acquaintance or the hopes I entertained of being his wife. Today's edition announced

Not only had Grandma's dramatic love story turned out to be a story of deceit and sadness, but I recognised the name of Henry Tillerman.

A quick internet search confirmed him to be the man who later bought out the paper and became one of Britain's most powerful media figures, but he went bankrupt in an attempted takeover and suffered a fatal heart attack soon after.

As for Grandma, I was desperate to know more. If the "H" in her early diaries was not Grandpa Hugh but Henry Tillerman, then I had to know when Grandpa came onto the scene. I felt as if my genetic heritage lay waiting in the wings of her journal.

Finally, the answer emerged, unequivocal and bold.

Today is a day I shall never forget. A new senior writer joined the paper: Hugh Edwards. He has considerable talent and has worked all over the country, but has

elected to return to his hometown of Stratford to be near his family.

This is a poorly paid position for him, yet he seems to be suffusing our local rag with energy and inspiration. He took the time on his first day to tour every department and meet every member of staff. It is unprecedented, truly!

A moment occurred that I cannot explain. He strode into our secretarial office, and I held my breath without even knowing who it was, but the instant he looked at me, I recognised him – not as Hugh Edwards but as "mine". Oh, it makes no sense at all, but there it is.

He introduced himself to each of us, and asked if I might show him around the rest of the works. At the end of this afternoon, he took his leave and said, "I feel that I know you already, Iris. I have the strangest sense there's more than one reason I find myself back in Stratford."

Maybe he is sentimental. Maybe I am being ridiculous. So why does it feel more natural than H's cold logic?

I found myself laughing out loud at my grandmother's reaction and could feel her delight and confusion in the very ink of her journals.

Today I have had another experience ➤

that I cannot explain: when I picked up my notebook, the pages were blank. I've always kept it separate from my everyday diary, a separate place for my heart's desires and secret prayers. I know I wrote them because I felt embarrassed to be so ambitious and selfish, but I wanted to put my longings into words and I believe in the power of writing.

When H first proposed, I had written my wish to be absolutely sure of love before accepting a proposal of marriage. I wished for my talents to be recognised. I wished to feel sure of my path in life.

Yet all these wishes have disappeared and I don't understand. Or at least, the only answer that comes to my heart makes no sense at all.

My original feminism feature used diary excerpts to illustrate the lives of working women over the century, and it grew into rather an obsession. It led to me becoming patron of a charity for equality at work, which has no pay or glory, but feels like a good thing to do.

I'm now a columnist and also working on a novel about a pioneering woman who becomes editor of a national paper in 1920s London, and – rather incredibly – I've been interviewed for a television series about equality at work.

I'm always busy, but I love it. It seems you can succeed in your career without losing your soul or your integrity, and I gravitate towards like-minded people, so I keep getting to work on great projects.

I'd spent two years trying to be less soppy – trying to be someone else

I understood. In so many ways, things become real when you put them into words; her prayers had been answered.

It is now five years since I inherited my grandmother's journals and many things have changed.

Firstly, my reaction to Grandma's love story showed me that I had been trying to suppress my romanticism to fit with Rob's logic. I'd spent two years trying to be less soppy – trying to be someone else.

So we sorted things amicably and went our separate ways.

Secondly, I bought my own journal and next to it, I keep the small golden notebook. To anyone else it's simply a blank book, but to me it's filled with wishes answered and dreams fulfilled.

There's probably a logical explanation for Grandma's disappearing text, but I prefer to ignore it. There's no harm having a little magic in your life.

A few boyfriends have materialised and faded, but my photographer buddy Charlie has started offering to collect me for interviews and there's a definite spark.

On his first visit here, he picked up Grandma's photo from the bookshelf and read the inscription on the back.

"Is this your grandma?" He smiled, holding up the photo beside my face and nodding. "I can see the likeness. *Our courting days,* how great is that? Makes me think of knights in shining armour.

"A guy could have felt like a superhero doing the whole courting thing. What do you think, Cathy? Will you report me for being sexist or can I bring you flowers and woo you the old-fashioned way?"

Ah, yes, I have a feeling he could work out very nicely indeed.

Just this morning, my face in the bathroom mirror caught me by surprise; it had the intriguing smile of someone who has a golden secret. 🆆

Ploughman's Scones

Ingredients (Makes 12)

- 450g self-raising flour
- ½tsp baking powder
- ½tsp salt
- 110g butter, chilled and cut into pieces
- 150g mature Cheddar cheese, grated
- 2tbsp chopped fresh chives
- 1 large egg
- Approx 200ml milk
- Wedges of Cheddar, cherry tomatoes and chutney, to serve

1. Preheat the oven to 220°C, fan 200°C, Gas Mark 7. Put a baking sheet into the oven to heat.

2. Sift the flour, baking powder and salt into a large mixing bowl. Rub in butter until the mixture resembles breadcrumbs. Mix in ¾ of the cheese. Stir in chives.

3. Beat the egg, then add milk to make up to 250ml. Add just enough to the rubbed-in mixture to make a soft (not sticky) dough. Knead lightly for a few moments. Turn on to a floured surface.

4. Roll out the dough to about 3cm thick. Use a 5-6cm plain cutter to stamp out rounds. Gather the trimmings together, re-roll and cut out more scones. Arrange on the hot baking sheet. Quickly brush the tops with egg mixture and sprinkle with the remaining cheese. Bake for 15-18 minutes until well-risen and golden brown. Cool for a few moments, then transfer to a wire rack to cool completely.

5. Serve the scones with wedges of Cheddar, cherry tomatoes and chutney.

RECIPE AND FOOD STYLING: SUE ASHWORTH PHOTOGRAPHY: JONATHAN SHORT

Last Bequest

Why on earth had Richard's old neighbour left him, of all people, to look after his beloved dog?

By Christine Sutton

Richard trudged down the steps from the solicitors' office and threw up his hands in despair.

"Now what am I supposed to do? Decline and I'm the worst person on the planet. Accept and I'm stuck with something I never wanted or asked for."

His neighbour Polly chuckled.

"You give in gracefully, Richard, that's what – same as I will. Oscar's a sweetie. You won't know you've got him most of the time. And I'm very much a cat person, so I'm happy to have Fluff."

"That's not the point, Pol," Richard grumbled. "I'm a free spirit – have been since Joan passed away. I go where I want, whenever I want. I can't do that with a dog in tow, can I?"

"Well, no, it's true they're a tie and free spirits needn't apply," she agreed. "But I'm intrigued by the notion that you are one. What does it entail for you exactly?

"Backpacking around Europe? Heading off into the wide blue yonder at a moment's notice? Cos I'm sure that's you I see nursing a pint in a corner of the Brickie's Arms every night!"

Single mum to a teenage daughter, Polly worked the evening shift behind the bar, while retired policeman Richard was ➤

a member of the Monday night quiz club and the Friday night darts team.

"It isn't the doing of it that's important," he said primly, "it's the *being able to* that matters."

She smiled indulgently.

"Well, if and when that day arrives, I'll have Oscar while you're off gallivanting in the Galapagos, or wherever.

"Meanwhile, accept your legacy with good grace, hmm?"

Behind them, the door opened and two people emerged, a woman and a boy of about twelve. The woman was immaculately dressed in a white woollen coat, tartan skirt and blue ankle boots.

"Oh – Mr Milton, Miss Lucas," she called out to them.

food too, and I believe he's put a little something in there towards future costs."

She gestured at the envelopes in their hands – letters from their old friend Larry, given to them by the solicitor as he'd outlined the bequest.

"Oh, there was no need for that, but it's kind of him to do so."

Richard glanced past her to the boy. His eyes were brimming with tears.

"I promise I'll take good care of Oscar," he said kindly.

"And Fluff will get lots of love and cuddles from us," Polly added. "My daughter, Rachel, loves animals. And if you ever want to come and visit…"

"Yes, or maybe meet up when I take Oscar for walks…"

"I don't care what she says, that lad needs to be able to keep in touch"

"I've left Brad with the solicitor so I could check with you both when it would be convenient to drop the animals off."

Her heels clicked as she hurried to join them. A cloud of perfume enveloped them and Richard suppressed a cough.

"I'm so glad Larry left them to you. We've had them at home since he died, but I couldn't look after them on a permanent basis."

"You haven't been," the boy cut in. "It's me who's been looking after them. They're no trouble."

The woman lowered her voice to a confidential whisper.

"It has been a worry, if I'm honest, knowing what to do for the best. I know Mattie wants to keep them, but…"

She gave a regretful headshake.

"But Larry clearly trusted you to look after them, so all's well. Would it be convenient if I drop them round this afternoon? I'll bring the bedding and

"I'm not sure about that," the woman hedged. "Best to make a clean break."

The hope that had flickered briefly on the boy's face died. Head down, shoulders hunched, he turned and walked back to the gleaming 4x4 parked at the kerb.

"Yours is the timbered house in Wayfarer Avenue, is that right, Mr Milton?" the woman said.

Richard nodded, feeling a sense of guilt, almost, at being part of this enforced animal snatch.

"And I'm just round the corner," Polly said helpfully. "Our properties are at right angles to one another. Neighbours but not, if you see what I mean! See you later then, Mrs Hill."

They headed for the car park.

"I don't care what she says, that lad needs to be able to keep in touch," Richard muttered. "He's lost his grandad and now he's going to lose the pets."

"Hmm. Not much in the way of mother love on show, was there?" Polly commented, glancing back.

The father, Brad, had joined them and was herding his family into the car, oblivious to the emotional tug-of-war that had just taken place.

"That's because Toyah's his stepmum," Richard explained. "She married Brad two years ago, after his first wife, Chloe, died. Larry always felt it was too soon, that Brad and Mattie were both still grieving. But Brad felt that Mattie needed a steadying influence in his life.

"He was nine when it happened and he felt the loss keenly."

Polly clicked the key fob.

"I can see the father's point of view, but all the lad really needs is love. I doubt he gets much from someone who looks more like a fashion plate than a mother."

"She can't be both?" Richard asked mildly with a raised eyebrow.

She gave a snort.

"Some, maybe, but not her. I bet the house is kept immaculate by some put-upon cleaner. A boy wouldn't dare breathe there, never mind have his mates round for video games and pizza."

"You can tell all that by looking at her?" Richard was incredulous.

Polly grinned.

"I wasn't always the threadbare ratbag you see before you. As a teen, I was convinced that happiness came from perfect grooming and a ton of make-up.

"Then I had my Rachel and everything changed. Kids want warmth and security and love by the bucket-load. It's a parent's job to provide that."

She opened the car door, then paused.

"Animals need that, too, come to think of it. Yours will be Oscar's third home in just a handful of weeks. Show the poor pup he's wanted, hmm?"

"I promise I will do my level best."

Richard raised a hand and walked on to his Volvo.

Opening the front door, Richard stepped into the hallway, seeing it through the eyes of the visitor who would soon be calling. The cosy nook of his imagination actually looked decidedly shabby, with cobwebs on the lampshade and scuff marks on the skirting. As for the garden…

He unlocked the kitchen door. Beyond the shed, the shoulder-high fence that divided his garden from Polly's was barely visible behind a mass of weeds and brambles. From memory, hers was a strip of grass dotted with planters, a more manageable layout for someone with not enough hours in the day.

He thought about what she'd said about Oscar's multiple homes. Larry had adopted the two animals from the rescue centre after staff explained they'd never been apart. Now they'd be living with different owners, never seeing one another unless the ageing Fluff could negotiate the fence.

He found himself wondering if a small pet flap might be the answer.

He hadn't done any woodworking in many a moon, but the equipment was all still there in the shed. He flexed his fingers, itching to start.

First things first though: he had to tackle those weeds.

Two hours later, the garden was transformed, Richard's access to the fence restored. He was about to go indoors for a well-earned cuppa when he spotted Polly coming out of her back door, a laundry basket under one arm.

"Hey, Pol," he called, beckoning her over. She came and stood on tiptoe to peer over the fence.

"Wow," she said. "Looks like you're taking the responsibilities of pet ownership very seriously." ➡

"Just didn't want the little chap hurting himself on the bramble thorns," he said defensively.

She patted his hand.

"I'm only teasing, Richard. It's a good thought, and you've done a brilliant job."

"Thanks, Pol. I was, uh, wondering whether I could install a sort of flap in the fence, so they could get through to see one another. I'd put a bolt on, so it could be closed at night."

Her eyes lit up.

"What a great idea. According to that letter, Fluff's at least ten, so jumping this high might not be ideal.

"And Rachel will love having Oscar come to visit. She wants to be a vet, you know," she added proudly.

"OK. And call in on the way back from the park for a coffee, alright?"

"Will do," he said.

He'd just put away the vacuum when the doorbell rang. Toyah Hill stood on the step, a cardboard box in her arms and a wretched-looking Mattie at her side.

He had the little dog clutched to his chest. Richard's heart went out to him.

"Come in, please, the kettle's just boiled," he said, relieving her of the box.

She'd changed out of the clothes she'd worn to the solicitor's and looked altogether different in jeans and a loose white sweater.

He elbowed open the door to the front room, cosy now with the heating on.

He had the little dog clutched to his chest. Richard's heart went out to him

"Clever girl," Richard commented.

"I haven't read my letter yet. Was there anything interesting in it?"

"Well, aside from a generous cheque towards vet bills, which was thoughtful of him, Larry said he was grateful that I'd agreed to take her on and he hoped you'd find it in your heart to take Oscar too. He'd be delighted to think you'd said yes."

Richard shrugged.

"How could I refuse? He was a good friend. I'm going to miss him."

"You'll still come to the quiz nights, though? Bring Oscar, just like he did."

"Of course," he answered, just as Polly's daughter Rachel appeared in the kitchen doorway.

"Mum, Mrs Hill's here with Fluff."

"She's not letting the dust settle, is she?" Polly arched her eyebrows.

Richard grinned.

"I'll be next, I'd better go in too."

She stepped away.

"Perhaps Mattie can suggest a good place for Oscar's bed. I thought maybe by the radiator. What do you think?"

The boy looked around.

"He slept in my room when he was with us, but this looks fine."

He bent down and let go of Oscar. The terrier set about an immediate exploration of his new home.

Richard set the box on the table and took out the dog bed. There was a squeak as he put it on the floor and Oscar came running to retrieve the rubber chicken hidden inside.

"He loves that," Mattie said fondly.

Richard gave his shoulder a squeeze.

"Like I said this morning, if you want to meet up in the park occasionally, it's no problem. There's a dog-friendly cafe there. I can stand you a hot chocolate."

Mattie turned a hopeful gaze to Toyah.

"I could maybe cycle over here after school sometimes."

Richard waited, expecting another knockback. To his surprise, she smiled.

"Thank you, Mr Milton. I feel this has all rather been dumped on you out of the blue, so it's kind of you to be so accommodating."

"Not at all," he said. "It's taken this to make me realise how much of a rut I've been in. I think Larry saw it long before I did and that's why he's done what he has.

"He was a wise old bird."

In the kitchen, the back door creaked in the breeze. Oscar's ears pricked up and he trotted off to investigate.

"Why not get his ball from the box, Mattie?" Toyah suggested. "You can go outside and play."

A moment later, he and Oscar were tearing around the garden.

"I can't tell you how much I've been dreading today," Toyah murmured, watching from the doorway. "Mattie has become so attached to Oscar – well, to both of them actually. They really seemed to be helping his recovery, but Brad wouldn't hear of keeping them, sadly."

Richard's jaw dropped. "You mean, it's not you who didn't want them?" ➜

She turned sharply, looking affronted.

"No! Why does everybody think that? Polly said the same. I told her I'd have loved to keep them, but Brad feels they'd be too much a tie if we want to go away."

"Well, pets are, aren't they – but they're worth every penny of the kennel fees if you ask me."

Richard handed her the tea, still adjusting to the new reality.

"Um, forgive me for saying so, but it seemed to me this morning as if Mattie believed it was your idea not to keep them. He seemed quite resentful."

She leaned against the door jamb, hands cupped around the mug.

"Better that he gets stroppy with me than with his dad.

Outside, Oscar was trying to drag a bramble cutting from the pile by the shed. Hearing Mattie laughing, Toyah's expression softened.

"You're right," she said, pushing herself away from the wall. "And between you and me, I've been working on Brad, trying to persuade him to let Mattie have a puppy. It's a month to his birthday and I really think Brad might agree."

She called to Mattie and he came running, breathless but happier. Richard led them into the hall and opened the door. Scooping Oscar into his arms, he walked to the gate and watched Toyah drive away with new respect.

That evening, Richard took Oscar for his first trip to the park.

"Funnily enough, Polly made the same offer. We had a lovely chat, actually"

"They've always been so close. Naturally, given what happened. I'd hate for that to change."

Richard stared, seeing her with new eyes. This wasn't someone heavy-handedly trying to take on the mantle of a much-missed mother, but a woman struggling to do her best in a difficult situation.

"You'd be welcome to visit too, you know," he murmured. "You could come for dinner. I'm told I do a mean lasagne."

"I'd like that, thank you. And, funnily enough, Polly made the same offer.

"We had a lovely chat, actually. I said I envied her relationship with Rachel. She's such a lovely girl.

"She even offered to help Mattie with his schoolwork. With everything that's happened, he's got a bit behind."

"She's a bright lass," Richard agreed. "And Mattie will be fine, you'll see. Things have a habit of working out, if you just give them time."

The sun was setting, silhouetting the trees starkly against a sooty pink sky. He hadn't been able to bring himself to come here since the last time with Joan.

Now, strolling by the lake, he breathed in the scented night air and thought how much he'd missed it.

Thirty minutes later, he was heading back up the street towards Polly's. Should he knock, or leave it? He was still standing undecided when the door opened.

"I hoped you'd come," she called. "I wanted to tell you about Toyah. I take it all back, she's a sweetheart."

He went closer.

"I know. We had an interesting chat."

Fluff came padding down the stairs. She greeted Oscar with a meow and the two animals rubbed faces.

Watching them, it dawned on Richard that, rather than a burden, Larry's bequest was actually a gift – one he'd be enjoying the benefits of for many years to come. Ⓜ

Brain Boosters

Sudoku

					7			
		7	1			9	8	2
2			4					6
4			5		1			
7	9					5		
6			8		7			
3			7					9
		1	6			8	5	4
						2		

Fill in each of the blank squares with the numbers 1 to 9, so that each row, each column and each 3x3 cell contains all the numbers from 1 to 9.

Turn To Page 171 For Solutions

Word Wheel

You have ten minutes to find as many words as possible using the letters in the wheel. Each word must be three letters or more and contain the central letter. Use each letter once and no plurals, foreign words or porper nouns are allowed. There is at least one nine-letter word.

The Photograph

There are different kinds of family ties… and all of them to be cherished, especially on this day

By Lynda Franklin

A photograph stands on my mother's sideboard in a dark mahogany frame. Every time I visit her, I take a moment to look at it and smile at my pretty young mother in her wedding dress.

She looks slightly self-conscious at being the centre of attention – head tilting to one side in the same gesture I make when I'm feeling awkward.

Her dress is typical '80s – big, puffed sleeves and a flouncy skirt. Her blonde hair is piled on top of her head with soft tendrils curling down and she's holding a small bunch of freesias.

We have the same eyes – it's uncanny how genes work to create almost identical parts in bodies that are connected.

I wasn't lucky enough to inherit her beautiful blonde hair, however. Mine is fine and auburn like my father's.

He stands next to her, red-headed and impossibly young-looking. Unlike my mother, he grins confidently into the camera. He still does! Dad loves having his photo taken, for some reason.

"Cup of tea, love?" Mum comes into the living room and plonks a tray down on the coffee table. It's full of china mugs, plastic cups for the children, assorted plates and a large Victoria sponge. ➤

"Careful," I murmur automatically as Olivia and Ted go to grab their drinks.

"I want cake," Ted says.

He's four and hasn't yet mastered the art of waiting to be asked.

"You have to wait," Olivia tells him in her best grown-up voice. Thank goodness I've got through to one of my children.

"Nanny will cut it in a minute," I say, turning from the photo.

Mum's already cutting slices. Dad stirs the pot and does his usual complaining that the tea's too weak.

Eventually we're sitting on comfy chairs in front of the fire – it's a chilly day for March. The children are alternating between eating cake, spilling drinks and building Lego on the floor.

writing," I say softly. "I love the card."

"He ruined it." Olivia gives a shrug and then continues with her Lego creation.

Mum grins at me and I roll my eyes.

"Better put another log on the fire," Dad says for the umpteenth time.

We both laugh, and I take a bite of Mum's delicious cake.

I am an only child. When you have your mother's exclusive attention all your life, you can't fail to grow up feeling loved and important.

My memories of childhood are the wafting smells of dinner cooking, a radio playing softly somewhere in the background and my mum's quick smile as she opened the door to me.

That, and the photograph on the

I remember looking across the room at my mother and feeling confused

It's a typical Mother's Day. We don't want to book a fancy restaurant or have an expensive day out. We are content to be in each other's company, chatting and enjoying the warmth of Dad's brand-new log burner which he absolutely adores.

"Great, isn't it? Really throws the heat out," he says for the hundredth time.

"They aren't good for the environment," I remind him.

"We only light it on special occasions," he says defensively.

"Today's special, isn't it?"

Olivia looks up from her Lego. Her face is glowing in the heat of the flames and her long blonde hair is shining.

She tilts her head – unsure – and for a split second I see my mother's expression.

"Very special darling," Mum tells her. "A special day for mothers everywhere."

"We made Mummy a card, but Ted scribbled on it and ruined it."

"He wasn't scribbling, Livvie, he was

sideboard in its dark mahogany frame.

I don't know how old I was, but as soon as I was able to see over the top of the sideboard I became aware of the photograph. I remember Dad picking me up and pointing at himself in the picture.

"Know who that is, Hayley?" he asked.

I looked at the grin and red hair and of course I knew who it was.

"Daddy!" I said, and he laughed.

I looked at the lady beside him in a big cream dress. I loved her thick pale hair, and I loved that somehow even though I didn't have thick pale hair, I still looked like her. I didn't have the same upturned nose, but our eyes were identical.

There was so much about her that looked familiar – and yet she wasn't.

I remember looking across the room at my mother and feeling confused. She looked so different from the pretty lady in the picture.

"Mummy," I said. Because it had to be.

Can I have some more cake, please?" Olivia is on her best behaviour because her teacher told them they must all be nice to Mummy on Mother's Day.

"A small piece," I tell her.

She tilts her head and smiles and my stomach rolls. She looks so much like my mother now, it's uncanny.

I know Mum has seen my look and she knows what I am thinking. She cuts Olivia a small slice of cake and passes it to her.

"Can we see the big book later?" Olivia asks.

"If you like," I tell her. "Later."

"I want to see the big book now!" Ted says immediately.

"We're looking at the big book later, Ted," Olivia announces sweetly.

I'm not sure how long this behaviour is going to last, so I soak it up and relax.

"Anyone want another cuppa?" Mum asks, looking around.

Dad nods, then gets out of his chair to throw yet another log on his precious fire.

I was probably five years old. Earlier than that, I would never have remembered or understood what I was being told.

Mum was good at telling stories. She would use different voices for the characters and sometimes I would be so drawn into the story I almost forgot it was my mum reading it.

But this story – the story she told me when I was five years old – was told in a soft voice that didn't change. There were no dramatic words or funny laughs or sound effects, just the pleasant sound of her voice telling me the most important story of my life.

"Once upon a time, there was a lady called Belinda," she began. Her eyes were bright and she said she had a cold. I thought having a cold was a nuisance because it meant she had to keep dabbing them all through the story. "Belinda was

as pretty as a princess," she said, "with long golden hair and a lovely smile."

"Did she meet a prince?" I said.

"Sort of – yes."

"Did they live happily ever after?"

Mum's cold got worse when I said that, and she pulled out a tissue and blew her nose. She wiped her eyes, pulled me closer and carried on talking.

"Belinda married her prince and they had a beautiful baby girl together. When the baby was just a few months old, Princess Belinda became very ill."

"That's sad."

"Yes – it was."

"Did she die?"

"Yes, she did." Mum coughed quietly. "But thankfully, she still had a special wish left over from the baby's christening."

"Like Sleeping Beauty?"

"Just like Sleeping Beauty."

"So what did she wish for?"

"She wished for a kind new mummy to come along and look after the baby… and her prince."

"Did she come?"

"Yes she did."

"So then did they live happily ever after?" I asked her.

"Yes – they were all very happy. But they never forgot Belinda or the special wish she'd made."

It was the start of my slow and natural realisation that I'd once had another mother. That she was young and pretty and lived on in the expressions and characteristics of myself and my children.

It was nice to feel that although I had never known her, I carried a part of her with me always.

I could not have wished for a better mother than the one Belinda wished for me. I watch her pouring out the tea and chatting happily with the children and feel a surge of love for her.

"Can we look at the big book now?" ➤

Olivia asks. Mum fetches it from inside the sideboard and places it on the table.

"Clean hands?" she asks, and the children nod seriously. They sense that this book is important – special – one to be looked after.

Carefully Olivia turns the first page.

"I love this – look! It's Grandad with Belinda at the seaside. You look funny, Grandad, in your swimming trunks."

I've lost count of the times I've looked at this book over the years, scanning the photos of my young, handsome dad with Belinda. It's one of my very first memories – sitting with my father and scrolling through the big book.

The final one is of Belinda.

Well – Belinda's full name was Belinda Edwina. Edward, Edwina. You see?"

He thinks about it for a second, then goes off to play with his Lego.

"Oh, look out – the fire needs topping up," Dad says, jumping out of his chair.

"Dad for goodness' sake, I'm sure you're burning too many logs."

"You can't burn too many, Hayley."

"More cake, love?" Mum asks me.

"Thanks, Mum."

As always, I brought two bunches of flowers today. I gave the bunch of deep red roses to Mum. She put them in her best crystal vase and stood them on a small table in the corner of the room.

The freesias are put in a vase next to the photograph that sits on the sideboard.

I am so grateful Mum and Dad kept this book for me. It makes me feel complete

Her fresh, young face is slightly obscured as she looks down at the small baby girl in her arms. I'm wrapped in a white crochet shawl that she made herself and I know she is feeling nervous because I can see the tilt of her head once again.

I love this photograph and am so grateful Mum and Dad kept this book for me. It makes me feel complete.

"I've got hair like Belinda, haven't I, Mummy?" Olivia states.

I reach forward and stroke the long, blonde curtain falling down her back.

"You have, Livvie," I say.

"And you have her eyes."

"What have I got?" Ted demands.

Mum smiles at him.

"You've got something very special, Ted – you have her name."

"My name's not B'linda!" he says indignantly.

Mum tickles him gently.

"Your full name is Edward, isn't it?

They are colourful and bright, as Belinda's must have been all those years ago.

I have always loved freesias and now I know why.

"Happy Mother's Day, Mum." I lift my cup of tea to her in a toast.

"And you, Mummy!" Olivia says quickly, searching for her drink.

"And B'linda Ted," Ted says.

I want to laugh, but his little face is so serious and I am aware that this is the first year he will begin to understand. I glance at the photograph on the sideboard.

"To mothers everywhere," I say.

"Mothers everywhere!" they all shout.

The big book is put away for another year and Dad is on the floor now building Lego with the children. Mum and I sit and watch. It's been our usual Mother's Day – not fancy, just tea and cake and being together. And when it's time to leave, I will give Mum a hug, blow Belinda a kiss and think again how very lucky I am. 🅜🅦

Brain Boosters

Codeword

Each letter of the alphabet has been replaced by a number. The numbers for the first name of our pictured celebrity are given. Work out which number represents which letter in the grid to reveal which BBC guessing game was presented by Stacey Dooley.

6	26	22	3	15	10	4	9	8	25	3		3	12	12
3		15		20		15		24		2		24		10
8	15	20	24	5		18	4	24	8	2	3	6	9	20
17		14		4		5				8		26		20
3	25	3	24	10	5		2	8	24	1	3	15	3	11
		21								5		3		10
12	26	9	21	19								3	11	1	3
26														6
15	3	3	16							12	4	6	8	6
10		7		19								26		
3	24	21	15	20	4	21	19		6	9	4	21	3	5
6		10		15				13		8		21		20
23	26	4	11	15	26	22	10	3		4	19	3	4	11
26		8		20		3		3		15		6		3
3	10	18		15	3	4	22	22	15	4	8	6	4	10

S T A C E Y

A B C D E F G H I J K L M N O P Q R S T U V W X Y Z

1	2	3	4 E	5 A	6 Y	7	8 S	9	10	11	12	13
14	15	16	17	18	19	20	21 C	22	23	24 T	25	26

| 9 T | 19 | 8 S | 6 | 8 S | 6 | 18 | 5 Y | 19 | 20 | 26 | 6 S | 3 E |

Turn To Page 171 For Solutions

Pear, Walnut And Blue Cheese Salad

Ingredients (Serves 2)

- ◆ 2 handfuls of mixed salad leaves, washed
- ◆ 60g walnut halves
- ◆ 2tsp mixed seeds
- ◆ 1 ripe pear, cored and sliced
- ◆ 1 small red apple, cored and chopped
- ◆ 80g Stilton

Dressing:

- ◆ 3tbsp walnut oil or olive oil
- ◆ 2tbsp lemon juice or white wine vinegar
- ◆ 1tsp clear honey
- ◆ ½tsp Dijon mustard
- ◆ Salt and freshly-ground black pepper

1 First, make the dressing. Mix together all the dressing ingredients and season with salt and pepper.

2 Arrange the salad leaves on 2 serving plates. Toast the walnut halves and seeds in a dry frying-pan for 1-2 minutes, tossing occasionally.

3 Arrange the pear slices and apple chunks on the salad leaves and crumble the Stilton over the top. Scatter the walnuts and seeds over the salads, drizzle with the dressing and serve.

Give yourself generous handfuls of salad with a wide variety of different leaves – this will ensure you get lots of nutritional benefits

RECIPE AND FOOD STYLING: SUE ASHWORTH PHOTOGRAPHY: JONATHAN SHORT

Fall For It

The romantic getaway was make-or-break for their big day – but could they ever agree on the perfect wedding?

By Lauren Rebbeck

The thick aroma of pumpkin spice flooded the tiny rental cottage. Orla watched over the brim of the wonky ceramic mug, as Rory frowned at her phone screen. He mocked her for packing their coffee machine and pods to bring on their getaway, but he wasn't complaining about his seasonal beverage now, was he?

"That's a lot of money for a cake," he grumbled, handing her glittery orange iPhone back.

"It's not just a cake! It's our wedding cake," Orla stressed. Although, secretly, she agreed with Rory. How good could this chocolate cake be to warrant its triple-figure price tag?

going to actually get married... and even that was up for debate after three days of bickering. Rory refilled Orla's mug and kissed her wavy hair, before poking at the logs in the wood burner. Or maybe she'd keep him, she thought tenderly. She loved every bone in his indecisive body.

They'd escaped to the country and rented a cosy woodland cottage. No work emails, no imposing relatives insisting on inviting their third cousin's best friend's spouse to the evening do, and no distractions! The plan was to nail down the details of their big day, enjoy some pub lunches and snuggle by the fire.

Orla returned to her phone, opening another wedding blog as Rory got up and grabbed his coat.

"Don't you have to be royalty to get married in a cathedral?"

"I told you, Auntie Barb said she'll make our wedding cake for us."

Rory raised his eyebrows hopefully.

Auntie Barb meant well, but she did get rather flustered under pressure.

Orla remembered last Christmas when Auntie Barb hosted, and mistook the chilli flakes for sprinkles.

"Two words for you," Orla held up two rust-manicured fingers. "Spicy. Trifle."

Rory winced. "Fair enough. But there must be some middle ground between food poisoning and bankruptcy?"

"Hmm," Orla grumbled, scrolling again. So far, the only nuptial decision the pair had agreed upon was that they were

"Come on, future Mrs. You need some fresh air and fresh eyes on all this wedding stuff."

He grabbed her plum coat and wide brimmed hat from the staircase banister.

"How about the cathedral? Think how dramatic our wedding photos would be!" Orla thrust her phone into Rory's face.

"Don't you have to be royalty to get married in a cathedral?" Rory plonked her hat onto her head, covering Orla's eyes.

"You're not actually a princess," Orla could hear him whisper, before he was muffled by the groan of the ancient oak front door opening.

They batted ideas back and forth as

they meandered down the hillside towards the village in the valley basin. With each footstep, the gentle lobbying of ideas became more contentious, until by the time they stomped across the stone bridge into the village, the pair were throwing absurd suggestions at each other.

"Why not just get married in a Bavarian castle? You could be flown in by pink unicorns," Rory cried.

"Or we could just do it at the bus station? I bet we could even get a discount if you flash your daysaver!" Orla hurled back, her boots clip-clopping against the cobblestones. "Maybe you should use it now to go back to London!"

Rory shook his head and made a swift escape into the nearest shop. Recognising his fiery fiancée's cues, he knew it was time to let her simmer. Orla stomped onwards, feeling smug that he had sought refuge in the haberdashery. She dipped into the next shop that was a suitable distance from her infuriating fiancé.

An intoxicating wave of scented wax washed over her. She ducked down as she browsed the rows of locally produced candles lining the shelves, lest she bump her head on the rafters.

She lingered around the seasonal shelf, breathing in the charcoal scent of Bonfire Bonanza and Sticky Toffee Pudding.

Choosing a spicy cinnamon three-wick candle, she headed for the till, where she begrudgingly purchased a bag of homemade salted caramel toffee. Rory's favourite.

Warm again in the cosy cottage, Orla listened to the rain pattering against the window and looked out into the darkening sky. Despite herself, she worried about Rory, alone in this unfamiliar boggy, terrain. He was a city boy, never so much as camping in the back garden. He'd once complained an open-top bus tour of London was "too much outside" for him.

Orla was up, searching for a flashlight, when she heard the reassuring groan ➜

of the front door. She nearly tackled Rory right out of his wellies.

"I'm so glad you're safe! I could kill you!" She kissed his chilly face. "I'm sorry! This wedding stress is making me crazy."

Between relieved smiles and smooches, Rory shrugged his fiancée and his soggy coat off.

He then wrapped a delicate crocheted scarf around Orla's shoulders.

"I got you this to apologise. The lady in the haberdashery made it herself."

He grinned sheepishly.

Orla beamed at him. "You know me so well." Then she handed over the homemade toffee, and ran the fine cream yarn of her scarf between her fingers.

"It's so beautiful, it must have taken her ages to finish!"

Rory was already stuffing the toffee into his mouth. "This won't take me ages to finish, though!"

He smiled, his teeth cemented together by caramel. His lips were salty and sweet when he kissed Orla.

As they lay by the fire, snuggled in nothing but a heavy knitted blanket and Orla's scarf, Rory apologised again.

"I'm sorry for being a grump. I want you to have the wedding of your dreams.

"I just don't want us to lose sight of what's important in a glitter bomb of prosecco and diamonds and expensive nonsense we can't afford.

"All that matters is that we become husband and wife… And that bit's free."

Orla leaned in and whispered, "Nope, we still have to pay the registrar."

She giggled at Rory's groan.

"I know I've been going over the top. I just want our big day to be perfect."

"Nothing's perfect, love," Rory reasoned, pulling her to him using the cream crochet scarf.

"Thank you again for my beautiful present," Orla cooed, the wool soft against her skin. "I love handmade things, they're so special. You can really feel the love that goes into them."

Rory reached past her and grabbed a piece of homemade toffee that had rolled under the couch, stuffing it into his mouth.

He laughed at Orla's horrified expression.

"Mm, I can really taste the love!"

That evening had been wonderful. Orla had felt so connected to Rory, entwined in each other and her special scarf (that she had worn every day since.)

But as the week went on, Rory was increasingly distracted. He'd been on his phone on and off all day, engrossed in whatever forum he'd stumbled on. He wasn't texting anyone, there was no signal up here, Orla's paranoid brain reasoned.

Was he avoiding wedding discussions? Hoping if he just ignored Orla's onslaught of suggestions, she might cave and they could elope at the registry office? Or had he decided it was all too much bother and he didn't want to get married at all now?

On their last day in the cottage, Orla skimmed her felt hat at Rory who was lazing on the sofa, frowning at his phone.

"Fancy a walk into the village? We can see if they've made any more toffee."

Rory grunted and shook his head, barely flinching as the hat landed on him. On her way out, Orla slammed the oak door so loudly, she guaranteed he flinched.

Twilight was settling over the valley as Orla dawdled back towards to cottage. She walked slowly, partly because her feet ached in her inappropriate (and now ruined) suede boots, and partly because she couldn't stand the thought of being ignored by Rory again. Or arguing with him. This wedding, this trip was supposed to be about celebrating their love, but Orla felt more alone than ever.

She pulled her trench coat around her, her sigh freezing in the crisp October air.

The lights were all on in the cottage, but no Rory. No fire crackling in the log burner. The cottage was freezing as well as lonely. Maybe Rory had enough of her and had gone back to London.

Why was she so relentless? Well, she'd need to be self-sufficient if she was going to be single again. So she headed towards the edge of the woods to grab some logs for the fire. No point being sad and cold.

But approaching the log shed, she spotted tiny golden lights floating among the trees. A fairy gathering? Entranced, she couldn't help but walk towards them.

Maybe this really was magic! The lights got brighter as she neared… illuminating an anxious Rory. He was lit by rows of fairy lights strung between the trees, raindrops shimmering as they fell. Orla was speechless – and curious.

She clung onto Rory's arm, as he led her to a rickety wooden table in the centre of the glen, sliding her into a fur-lined chair. It was the dining table from the cottage! She hadn't noticed the missing furniture in her rampage of self-reliance.

An unfamiliar lace tablecloth adorned it, and set on top was a wonderful spread of pumpkins, countless creamy, waxy candles of irregular sizes, a smattering of pine cones and coffee beans. In the centre was a very familiar orange wellie… her own! It was stuffed with a bouquet of beautiful dried flowers: a makeshift vase.

Orla's mouth watered as the scent of pumpkin soup wafted up from the warm bread bowl, placed beside a red maple leaf place card. "Orla" was scrawled in Rory's familiar scribble on the leaf.

The gentle melody of their favourite folk song was barely audible above the rustle of the wind in the trees.

"What is this?" Orla whispered, intoxicated by the romance.

"It could be our wedding… if you like," Rory suggested, haltingly. His brow furrowed and he held out a bouquet: a rainbow of dried leaves. She gripped it, bewitched and bewildered.

"I mean, not right now! I know you want your mum there!" Rory shook his head, rattled.

"I'm no good with words. Which is why I did this!" He gestured around him.

"I wanted to show you what I've been so preoccupied with all week. When you said you loved that homemade scarf because it was special, a light bulb went off.

"But how could I pitch a wonky, imperfect, crafty wedding to you, after all the luxurious things you've been suggesting? I needed to show you how I envisioned marrying someone as special, wonderfully flawed and unique as you… surrounded by things that were special, wonderfully flawed and unique."

"How?" Orla managed to gasp, clutching the leaf bouquet.

"YouTube DIY videos mainly. That's why I've been glued to my phone," Rory shrugged. "And I had a little help. Ida – she owns the haberdashery and made your scarf – has been dipping candles all week. We need to leave her an excellent Tripadvisor review, by the way."

Orla laughed, breaking from her trance.

"So what do you say, Orla? Will you marry me… like this?"

"I'm going to need a new pair of wellies." Orla nodded at the centrepiece between them. "Think you can find me a pair in white?"

She threw the leaf bouquet into the air and clasped her hands around Rory's relieved face, kissing him hard as rusted leaves flitted in the air around them. 🅜🅦

Brain Boosters

Missing Link

The answer to each clue is a word which has a link with each of the three words listed. This word may come at the end (eg **HEAD** linked with **BEACH, BIG, HAMMER**), at the beginning (eg **BLACK** linked with **BEAUTY, BOARD** and **JACK**) or a mixture of the two (eg **STONE** linked with **HAIL, LIME** and **WALL**).

ACROSS

8 Den, Paw, Share (5)
9 Buying, On, Purchase (7)
10 Orient, Train, Wish (7)
11 Guy, Off, Skipping (5)
12 Dental, Full, Heat (9)
14 Gentle, Handle, Slaughter (3)
15 Group, Ice, Iron (3)
16 Rhyme, Subjunctive, Tense (9)
19 Cycle, Dirt, Race (5)
21 Edge, Lane, World (7)
23 Holiday, Language, Medieval (7)
24 Beer, Lout, Shandy (5)

DOWN

1 Hall, Prince, Square (6)
2 Disaster, Set, Stranger (8)
3 Emerald, Fair, Lake (4)
4 Paper, Scar, Toilet (6)
5 Computer, Smooth, Tour (8)
6 Bicycle, Hair, Paper (4)
7 Admiral, Half, Mandela (6)
13 Cap, Lateral, Wishful (8)
14 Race, Staff, Team (8)
15 Carotid, Major, Pulmonary (6)
17 Ear, Head, Mobile (6)
18 Chaos, Literary, String (6)
20 Open, Present, Race (4)
22 Fore, Off, Tale (4)

Turn To Page 171 For Solutions

Hidden word in the shaded squares: _____

Kriss Kross

Try to fit all of the listed words back into the grid.

4 letters	5 letters	8 letters	10 letters
ABUT	AVERT	PORTABLE	AUTOMOTIVE
PAPA	ELBOW	PREGNANT	EXPATRIATE
PATH	EXIST	UNTANGLE	**11 letters**
ROAN	**7 letters**	**9 letters**	PROLETARIAT
	AVARICE	ANTENATAL	REGIONALIST
	TWEETER	OFFHANDED	

Turn To
Page 172 For
Solutions

A Time For Healing

Many years before, the war brought its own traumas – but family divisions had left scars, too...

By Juliet Greenwood

O ver the years, Paris had become beautiful once more.

Nancy sat on a bench in the Jardin des Tuileries that spring morning, feet aching from days of exploring the old familiar sights.

This time, the walk down the Champs-Élysées to the Arc de Triomphe, and even standing at the base of the Eiffel Tower, had been tinged with the images of Hitler inspecting the captured city in photographs and newsreels. But the steep steps of Montmartre had been much the same as she remembered from her childhood, bustling with the noise and colour of artists painting portraits of visitors, or deep in discussion in the winding network of cafés beneath the imposing white dome of Sacré-Cœur.

Nancy turned her eyes once more to the petit bateaux, as the children pushed the little toy boats towards the centre of the circular pond with the aid of long sticks. One stroke, and each colourful sail set off bravely on its adventure, returning to the smooth sides of the pond, to be pushed away again.

Once – so long ago it felt now – that had been her; the little girl in the blue ➤

dress, dark plaits tied with a matching ribbon, wielding her stick so confidently, while her father helped her younger brother with his own small boat.

Nancy knew she was lucky that her brother had survived the fighting in France, when so many had been lost.

Those years had turned Paul from the rowdy lad always in trouble and sending her mother into despair, into a gentle, taciturn man, whose world revolved around his wife and their three girls, with every free moment lovingly tending the flowers and vegetables in his allotment.

Paul was still haunted by what he had seen. She'd known, even when she'd suggested it, that he would not return to France again. She had not pressed him, understanding that he could not bear to revisit the memories, not even of the happier days of their childhood stays.

Nancy sighed. Around her, she could see visitors and Parisians alike strolling along the wide paths spanning out from the pond, enjoying the sunshine and the fresh greening of lawns.

At the edges, pink blooms of magnolia glowed between the new leaves of the surrounding trees, set off by the brilliance of red and yellow tulips and the soft whites and purples of pansies.

From further away came the murmur of the city, with the business of traffic that, along with the glimpses of the Eiffel Tower between tall buildings, she had always associated with Paris.

Watching the little boats being urged to and fro, Nancy felt something inside her shift. The last time she had been in the City of Light had been just after the war, when, despite the brilliance of the summer heat, it had felt a very dark place indeed.

Beautiful, broken Paris that had borne the signs of war and occupation both in its battered streets and in the haunted faces of its people. A Paris that, like the ruined communities around, had survived, but at a terrible cost and with memories that would haunt a lifetime.

She had felt certain that Paris would never return to the magical city of childhood visits to Mum's family in the village just outside the city's reach, any more than she could imagine her home city of London recovering from the battering of The Blitz.

Yet London had sprung up again, more vibrant than ever now that the memories had been softened by time, accompanied by a sense of a better world being created, with even rationing finally a thing of the past.

The turning of the 1950s to the 1960s had brought a new energy in the air; a mixture of optimism and rebellion, with a sense that the old rules were there to be broken.

"It's time," she reminded herself under her breath. She had known it the moment she'd started to plan for this visit. Over the last few days, her courage had failed her.

What was the point? So much had been lost, surely it was time to finally let go and not stir up painful memories?

But now, sitting in the Jardin des Tuileries in the heart of Paris, she was certain. Finally, it was time to confront the past and see if there might, after all, be bridges left to be mended.

Nancy left her hotel early the next morning, taking her cream-coloured Mini with its GB plates through the city traffic, ignoring the impatient hooting and gestures from drivers outraged at the sight of a lone female daring to dart boldly between the cars. They hadn't seen her race down the King's Road in London, she thought with a grin, or seen her brave the chaos around Marble Arch, refusing to be intimidated by even black cabs and double-decker buses.

After all, she'd driven ambulances

during The Blitz, between hours using her fluent French and passable German to work as a translator for the War Office.

Nothing could ever be as terrifying as hurtling through the darkness of the blackout, the skeletons of what had once been homes lit by the harsh flicker of flames.

Once out in the long straight roads of the countryside, Nancy found she still knew the way so well she had no need to consult the map laid out on the passenger seat.

Like Paris, the fields on either side appeared to have recovered from the passing of tanks and machine guns, and the bleak destruction of the fighting.

Between the new growth she caught glimpses of red-tiled villages crouched

work during the war had taken them, or by simply a desire to escape the memories of Nazi occupation. Even Mémé had been persuaded to join her cousin in Switzerland, living the rest of her life beneath the shadow of the Alps.

Nancy parked the Mini on the outskirts of the village and walked through the main street, nodding vaguely at the shopkeepers and housewives on their doorsteps who turned to stare at the stranger.

She didn't recognise them, apart from the elderly woman smoking a pungent Gitane at one of the tables set outside the café. Mme Ménard eyed her as if half-seeing the skinny English girl from before the war in the middle-aged woman in the pencil skirt and Dior jacket, appearing out

They had been magical evenings, the faces of adults glowing beneath lanterns

around the spire of a church, along with the occasional chateau, isolated in its formal grounds, a reminder of a grander time before the world fell apart.

The little village was much as she remembered from when Mum brought her each summer to visit Mémé, Nancy's grandmother. In each street there had been an aunt or a cousin, who had welcomed them with open arms.

There had been leisurely meals, the entire extended family seated either side of tables under the apple trees in the soft warmth as the sun went down.

They had been magical evenings, the faces of the adults glowing beneath lanterns hung on branches, while the children ran around and played in the grass. Who could have thought they would ever end?

The family had left now, its members scattered across the world where their

of nowhere.

The large manor house was still there at the far end of the street, protected by a high stone wall. Nancy's heart sank.

It looked as if Maison Des Lis had been abandoned, after all. The surrounding wall was crumbling in several places, allowing glimpses of the red-tiled roof and the faded blue shutters, more than one hanging off its hinges.

The tangle of abandoned garden was a blow to Nancy's stomach, telling of nature reclaiming the place over years.

She hesitated at the ornate iron gates, with their rusting pattern of abstract swirls curving over the regular pattern of lilies that had given the house its name.

The scent of lilies. That was her strongest memory of the Maison Des Lis. Mum's younger sister, Aunt Irène, had broken free of the 1930s expectation that women settled down to a lifetime ➡

of domesticity, to become a renowned horticulturalist. It was where Nancy had gained her own love for garden design, assisting Irène in the garden of the aristocratic Saunier family in the Maison Des Lis.

That was also where she had got to know the Saunier boys, Armand, Jean and Phillipe, along with their little sister Francine. All four had eagerly escaped the stifling grandeur of their home to make a show of taking an interest in the garden, with the excuse to race around in wild abandon among the fountain and the formal beds of roses set furthest away – and so largely invisible – from the house.

Ever since, the scent of lilies always sent Nancy straight back to those heady summer days, when none of them could have imagined what lay ahead.

the wall to be repaired." He eyed the house with faint disapproval. "Maybe this time he will stay."

Nancy's heart squeezed. Turning to peer through the gate, she could make out that the front door to the house stood open, with a small van in front of it, along with a bright red Citroën 2CV.

"Merci, thank you," she murmured.

It must be Jean who had returned, lord of the manor since the death of his elder brother. She paused, hand on the latch, as a middle-aged man with a shock of white hair emerged to retrieve a suitcase and a toolbox from the Citroën.

As he headed back inside, he turned, as if sensing her gaze. Yes, it was Jean alright, always the most handsome of the Saunier boys, still striking, with his frame filled out from boyish leanness into the

"You were the one who persuaded me to come to this godforsaken place"

"Madame?"

Nancy jumped, startled from her thoughts by an elderly man arriving with a wheelbarrow filled with tools and what appeared to be bags of sand and cement, which he deposited next to the broken piece of wall.

"The Sauniers," she asked in her best French, attempting to keep her voice free of emotion, "they never came back?"

"No, Madame," he replied warily.

This was clearly not a subject to be discussed with outsiders.

But Nancy had never been one to give up. "I used to visit here," she said, "before the war. I was told Armand was killed in the fighting. So, is it to be sold?"

The man's demeanour relaxed a little. She was not such a stranger after all.

"Not now, it seems. M. Saunier arrived a few days ago. He has given orders for

confidence of a man in his prime.

She reached to push the latch, to call out, to go towards him, to make the first move –

"Did you find it?" She stopped at the woman's voice, and the elegantly clad figure appearing at the doorway.

"Find it?"

"My purse," the woman replied impatiently.

"I must have put it somewhere when I stopped at the boulangerie."

"Women," said Jean good-humouredly. "What would you be without me, chérie?"

"Still the best hostess of dinner parties in Marseille," she retorted.

"You were the one who persuaded me to come to this godforsaken place."

"Aline…" He sounded hurt.

"Yes, yes, I know. I'm sorry." Aline

retrieved a purse from the footwell of the Citroën. "It was my choice too," she added, kissing him. "Although I hope you know the children may never forgive you."

Nancy let her hand fall. She had no right to intrude, bringing with her memories of pain. She was, in truth, an outsider. Even the elderly man had forgotten her in his repairing of the wall.

Slowly, she turned and made her way back through the village towards her car.

The petit bateaux bobbed and danced cheerfully on the pond as Nancy returned to the Jardin des Tuileries later that afternoon.

"Mummy!" Susy abandoned her boat to her little brother, plaits flying behind her and tied, like yesterday, in her favourite blue ribbon. "You were gone ever such a long time."

Nancy returned her embrace.

"Was I, darling?"

"Daddy said we can go right to the top of the Eiffel Tower once you're back."

Nancy smiled at her husband, who gave a wry grimace in ➔

acknowledgement that his daughter could twist him around her little finger.

"Then that's what we'll do," she said.

"Well?" he asked, eyes following Susy, as she raced back to her boat.

"Francine was right," Nancy replied.

"Jean is returning to Maison Des Lis. He's there now. The telephone can't have been reconnected yet."

He was still watching the boats.

"Did you speak to him?"

"No. But I think you should."

the Nazis' noses. I think maybe his determination to keep the Maison Des Lis became his own kind of resistance."

A cry of frustration from the pond sent her husband to help Jack, who was only five and whose boat, despite his sister's attempts to help, was going nowhere.

Yellow sail pushed out once more towards the centre, Phillipe returned.

Nancy could see the tense lines of his face had eased a little.

A rush of love went through her.

"He made it clear last time that the family will never accept you"

She felt him wince.

"I can't, chérie. It's too long, there were too many harsh words between us."

"Jean's still your brother, Phillipe. Francine has made her life in Australia, she won't be back. He's the nearest family you have."

He turned to her, frowning.

"He made it clear last time that the family will never accept you."

"Things change. I may not be French aristocracy, but I've worked my way up to being a garden designer to the rich and famous.

"That must be second best, surely?"

He smiled at that. Then the smile faded. "I can't forget what he did. Nor will the village."

"It must have taken guts for him to go back," she acknowledged. "But I'm not so sure you are right about the village. Mme Ménard still runs the café on the main street. She told me emotions have faded and things are never that simple.

"They can see that Jean did his best to keep the village safe from the occupiers.

"She said they didn't know at the time, but he managed to get several of the Jewish families away, right under

Despite the greying at his temples, he was still the young intelligence officer who had sought her out in London at the height of The Blitz. It had been the meeting of childhood friends, drawn together through loss and grief, and the destruction of both their countries by a seemingly implacable evil.

A meeting that had become a passionate grasping at life before the next bomb fell, or the expected invasion destroyed them all.

They had never thought, in those days, that the bonds forged would become a love to last a lifetime.

"I can take the children to visit Versailles tomorrow," she said.

"They'll enjoy that. Maybe Jean also wants to make peace."

Slowly, he nodded.

"But only if they accept all of us."

Nancy kissed him.

"The ties that bind families run deep, darling. Surely we can all let go of the past, for our children's sake."

"I hope so," he replied, smiling as Jack and Susy, boats forgotten in anticipation of their visit to the Eiffel Tower, arrived eager for their next adventure to begin. Ⓜ

Red Lentil, Spinach And Sweet Potato Curry

Ingredients (Serves 2)

- ◆ **1tbsp coconut oil or vegetable oil**
- ◆ **1 onion, sliced**
- ◆ **200g sweet potatoes, peeled and chopped into chunks**
- ◆ **1 red pepper, deseeded and chopped**
- ◆ **2tbsp Thai red curry paste**
- ◆ **400ml can coconut milk**
- ◆ **100g red lentils**
- ◆ **200ml vegetable stock**
- ◆ **2tbsp chopped fresh coriander**
- ◆ **50g young spinach**
- ◆ **20g plain cashew nuts**
- ◆ **Naan bread and coriander sprigs, to serve**

For the raita:

- ◆ **4tbsp plain yogurt (or non-dairy yogurt if vegan)**
- ◆ **2tbsp chopped cucumber**
- ◆ **1tbsp chopped fresh coriander**

1 Heat the oil in a large pan. Add the onion, sweet potatoes, and red pepper. Cook over a medium heat for 2-3 minutes, stirring.

2 Add the curry paste and stir through. Pour in the coconut milk. Add the lentils, stock, and chopped coriander. Simmer over a low heat for 20 minutes, until the lentils and sweet potatoes are tender. Add an extra splash of water, if needed.

3 Meanwhile make the raita by mixing the yogurt, cucumber and coriander together. Warm the naan bread following pack instructions.

4 Add the spinach to the curry and stir for 1-2 minutes until wilted. Season and serve with the raita and warm naan, sprinkled with cashew nuts and coriander sprigs.

RECIPE AND FOOD STYLING: SUE ASHWORTH
PHOTOGRAPHY: JONATHAN SHORT

Always In My Heart

Although long gone, a moment's reflection brings the family's beloved Nana Jo unexpectedly closer...

By Julie Dawn Baker

Every year on Mum's birthday, I post on Facebook – usually a simple "Happy Birthday, Mum", an old photo of her and a broken heart emoji. And every year, Mum's birthday post receives hundreds of "likes", "loves" and "cares".

Friends and family take the time to comment: "Beautiful picture", "I miss her too", "Your mum would be so proud of you, Amy!" Sometimes Mum's old friends,

who are now my friends on Facebook, message me privately with memories or words of sympathy and encouragement.

This year, instead of a portrait of Mum, I posted a photo of Dad and my youngest, nine-month-old Cala. I took it this morning before we went to put flowers on Mum's grave. Dad had arrived early, and he'd been watching the baby while I dropped my older two off at school. I came home to find Dad lounging on the floor with Cala, the two of them ➡

connecting in their own little world.

Before they even realised I was there, I'd captured the moment on my phone. A candid shot brimming with love.

I uploaded the picture right away. Even though Mum wasn't in it, it was perfect for her birthday photo because she would have loved seeing Dad and Cala together.

Of course, Mum would have been down on the floor with them, or perhaps she'd have taken the photo – a proud nana, that's for sure.

It's late morning before I get around to checking Facebook. "Shall we see if anyone liked the picture of you and

her baby blue eyes twinkling, lips glossy with drool.

There's a sparkly quality to the photo, and although I didn't apply a filter, the colours seem especially vivid. It's only when I examine the background of the picture, that I spot the image causing such a stir. A flash of light has bounced off the glass doors leading to the back garden, and in the centre of the golden, glittering halo is a face. A familiar face.

Mum's face.

Why didn't I notice this when I took the photo? How did I miss Mum's face at my window?

I don't really believe in ghosts or anything supernatural

Grandad?" I ask Cala, who is sitting in her highchair happily gumming some raspberries.

As it does every year, Mum's birthday tribute has garnered a huge number of responses. Unusually, amongst the "loves" and "likes", I note a smattering of "wows".

Assuming the open mouth emoji denoting surprise was accidently pressed instead of its neighbour, the sad face, I smile, knowing how easy it is to offend with a slip of the finger.

My smile fades though, when instead of the usual array of comments laced with sympathy and sadness, I find myself reading:

"Amazing!"

"Wow!"

Now, for his age, Dad's a good-looking guy, and Cala is one of the cutest babies on the planet, but the photo isn't wow-worthy.

Confused, I tap on the image and zoom in on Dad. He's starting to show his age, I realise, noticing his cheeks etched with deep wrinkles. Cala is chuckling at him,

And suddenly, the unexpected comments peppering my post make perfect sense. Mum has been gone for over 20 years now. Twenty-four years and seven months, to be exact. She died when I was 14. A lifetime ago.

Scooping up Cala, who squeals with indignation, I rush into the living room to see if Mum's outside in the garden.

Of course, she's not.

Still clutching Cala, I sink into the armchair by the patio doors and turn back to my phone.

More comments have been added: "How did you do that? A special effect?" "What am I seeing here?!" A few people have openly suggested there might be an otherworldly explanation for Mum's face at the window.

For the record, I don't really believe in ghosts or anything supernatural, but I have experienced moments when I've suspended disbelief.

There was the time when Fleur, my 10-year-old, was still a baby. My husband, Kyle, had been away on a business trip and late one night Fleur wouldn't stop crying. I was at my wit's end, crying myself, when I'm sure I heard Mum's gentle voice telling me what to do.

"Warm some towels and lay Fleur on them on her tummy."

I'd quickly thrown some soft towels in the dryer, draped them over my knees, and lain Fleur on them. Amazingly, within minutes, she stopped crying, and – this is the strange part – I'd become aware of the delicate, sweet scent of Mum's favourite perfume, Angel, drifting in the air.

I'd told Dad about Mum's "angelic" intervention the next day.

"Ha! The old warm towels on the knees trick! I remember your mum doing that with you!'

"So, d'you think Mum knew I needed her and visited last night?" I'd asked him.

I should have known he wouldn't agree. A retired engineer, Dad always looks for the logical, scientific explanation.

"Your mum often used to tell you stories about when you were a baby. My guess is she'd told you how warm towels used to soothe you, and the remedy was logged in your memory banks waiting to be retrieved."

"But how do you explain the perfume, the whiff of Angel in the air?"

"Ah, Jo's signature scent. It's tempting to read too much into that, especially with a name like 'Angel', but you've worn that perfume, too, haven't you?"

"Not for ages now."

I'd worn it for a while after Mum died; it was like being wrapped in a hug and made me feel Mum was nearby.

"The oils and extracts in perfume can linger for a long time. Traces will have been on one of the fabrics and the warmth brought it out," Dad explained.

I'd wanted to argue with him, but knew his theories made sense.

There have been other sightings,

for want of a better word. I still get goosebumps when I recall Jasper, my six-year-old, excitedly telling me, "I saw Nana Jo go by on a cloud!" He'd been about four – old enough to be upset when I'd laughed. "I did see her!" he insisted. "She blew me a kiss. I blew one back, and she caught it." Mum had been a big blower, and catcher, of kisses.

Of course, Dad and Kyle, had a logical explanation. They were both quick to point out it was no coincidence Jasper saw his Nana Jo the day after we'd visited my grandparents, so Grandad could show clips from a digital remix he'd had made from all the old films and videos he'd taken of Mum over the years.

Nonetheless, to this day Jasper is certain he saw his Nana Jo.

Turning back to my Facebook post, I wonder what Dad and Kyle will make of one of Mum's old friends who has commented, "It's like Jo is peeking through a portal from the other side!"

I don't have to wait long. Dad replies almost instantly.

"Let's not get carried away. I'm pretty sure it's Amy's own reflection in the glass."

As if she's monitoring my post, there's an immediate reply to Dad from Gran. ➙

"Amy looks like our Jo, but that's not Amy."

A few minutes later, Dad replies, "Probably a reflection of the portrait of Jodie which Amy has on a side table."

I'm not convinced by Dad's theory.

In the framed picture of Mum, her expression is pensive, thoughtful. She's as beautiful as ever, but she's not smiling.

The face at my window is beaming. And Mum's portrait faces into the room, not towards the window.

I resist joining in the debate and sit Cala on the floor while I try to recreate the picture I took earlier.

Despite using a flash, no flash, shifting positions, doing whatever I can to make that illusive face appear, no joy.

When Cala starts to get fussy, I put her down for her nap.

As much as I want to keep on taking photos and monitoring the comments on Facebook, I need to bake the cake for Mum's birthday dinner tonight.

Tradition dictates that we have a rather retro Black Forest gateau – Mum's favourite. I use her recipe for chocolate cake – delish! I've just popped it into the oven when Dad calls.

His tone reveals that he's worried about me after all the furore on Facebook.

When I admit to trying to recreate Mum's face at the window, he launches into a full-scale debunk and talks about refracted light particles, convex – or was it concave – angles, needing to recreate the exact conditions under which the photo was taken, until I'm completely blinded by science, but still not entirely persuaded.

I'm relieved when the oven timer dings, and I have an excuse to hang up.

Cake on the cooling rack, a quick glance at the clock tells me I can make Mum's spaghetti sauce before Cala wakes.

Mum started teaching me to cook when I was quite young, and just like she did, once it's made, I simmer the sauce in my slow cooker to allow the flavours to mingle. As soon as the lid is on the pot, I reach for my phone. I'm amazed so many people have added to the debate my photo has prompted.

It's hard to tear myself away from all the comments on Facebook, but I reluctantly pocket my phone because I hear Cala stirring and see it's almost time to pick up the kids.

"Can we go to the swings at the park?" Jasper asks when he comes flying out of school.

"I don't think we've got time today, Jasper. We've got all the family coming over for dinner tonight. Oh look, here's Fleur. Let's head home, and you can both help me finish the cake."

"Please," he wheedles. "And after we've been on the swings, we can take Cala to see the ducks."

"I don't have any bread for the ducks, Jasper."

"I've got crusts in my lunchbox. I saved them!"

Jasper roots around in his backpack, pulls out his lunchbox and shakes it.

"I thought you always ate your crusts, Jasper! Nana Jo used to say, 'Eat your

Nana Jo fell in feeding the ducks when she was little," Fleur warns Jasper, who is lobbing crusts with gusto towards the ducks.

"And she got bitten by a swan when she was feeding the swans by the river," Jasper adds, drawing from the repertoire of Nana Jo stories that have become part of our family folklore.

It always makes me smile to hear the way my children talk about Mum as if they were there when these misadventures happened.

Of course, the kids don't remember the near-drowning any more than I do, but Mum used to remind me of it whenever I ventured too close to the edge, and I have dutifully repeated the story as a warning to Fleur and Jasper.

His lunchbox empty of crusts, Jasper runs off towards the swings. I repeat my earlier warning of 10 minutes playtime and add, "Then we have to head straight home to finish the cake for dessert."

"For Nana Jo's party!" Jasper shouts excitedly.

It always makes me smile to hear the way my children talk about Mum

crusts, it'll make your hair curl!'" Fleur never misses an opportunity to tease her brother about his mop of tight blond curls.

"Ten minutes on the swings, and then we have to go," I warn them when we arrive at the park.

"I'm going to feed my crusts to the ducks first," Jasper yells, throwing his bag on the ground and running off with his lunch box in the direction of the pond.

Struggling to push Cala's buggy over the bumpy grass, I tell Fleur to go with her brother. "Make sure he doesn't get too near the edge, Fleur!"

"Stand back, Jasper! Remember how

"Not exactly a party," I tell him. "Just the family coming for dinner."

After a bit of wrangling, and unashamed bribery – "Yes, you can whip the cream for the cake, Fleur, and yes, you can lick the beaters, Jasper" – I get the kids home. We're all ready by the time Kyle gets in, and Dad, my stepmum, Pam, and Gran and Grandad arrive for dinner.

"I'm so glad you've continued this birthday tradition, Amy," Gran says, giving me a hug.

Gran started inviting everyone to her house for dinner on Mum's birthday the first year after Mum died, but she's ➤

in her eighties now and finds it a bit too much. Besides, once we had the children, it was much easier to have everyone over to us.

"It's a bittersweet day. Good to keep Jo's memory alive, but sad she's not here to enjoy it," Gran says, then adds in a whisper, glancing pointedly towards the living room, "or maybe she is…"

"Ah, you saw all the speculation on Facebook earlier today," Kyle says. "Please don't say anything in front of the children."

"Yes," Dad agrees. "We don't want to fill their little heads with nonsense."

Gran bristles. "I'm not so sure it's nonsense. I'd say the proof was there for all to see."

granddaughter, Amy, and our wonderful great-grandchildren, Fleur, Jasper and Cala." Everyone raises a glass and chimes, "To Jo!" "To Mum!" "To Nana Jo!"

As it's a school night, no one stays late, and soon the house is quiet with everyone in bed. Although I'm tired, sleep doesn't come. When I hear Cala wake up, instead of settling her in the nursery, I take her to the living room. Without putting on a lamp, I pull back the curtains and peer into the darkness outside. Disappointed, I glimpse nothing more than my own blurred reflection staring back at me.

Aware of the weight of my phone in the pocket of my dressing gown, I can't resist taking a photo. Just in case. The burst of light from the flash startles Cala,

I don't need to see a hazy image of Mum to feel that she's nearby

"There are multiple explanations. You know where I stand on this matter–" Dad begins.

But Gran interrupts. "I do, and we'll have to agree to differ." Turning away, she flashes me a smile. "Now, let's get dinner served, something smells delicious. Spaghetti, if I'm not mistaken."

"Did someone say spaghetti? Yum!" Pam grins.

"Mum's special recipe?" Dad asks.

"Of course," I smile.

"You and your mum make the best spaghetti sauce,' Dad says. "Sorry Pam," he adds, looking contrite.

"Don't apologise, silly!" Pam laughs.

"I know Jo was a fabulous cook!"

Gran and Pam begin herding everyone to the table, food is dished out, and when we're all seated, as she does every year, Gran makes a toast.

She keeps it light and brief. "To Jo, who lives on in our beautiful

but she quickly snuggles back into the crook of my neck. Although I carefully scan each centimetre of the picture, I see no ghostly reflections or strange shadows.

Switching off my phone, I realise I don't need to see a hazy image of Mum to feel that she's nearby. If today has shown me anything, it's that Mum's spirit lives on in the shared memories of all the people she loved and those who love her still.

Yes, Mum is always with me, always in my heart.

My lips brush the top of Cala's silky head as I whisper, "Your Nana Jo might not be here, but there's a part of her in me and in you, and Fleur and Jasper. Not just DNA though. She's a part of our lives. Every day."

As I turn away from the window to return Cala to her room, I catch the faintest hint of the familiar scent of Angel enveloping us. I'm smiling as I murmur, "Happy birthday, Mum." Ⓜ

Brain Boosters

Sudoku

		3		5				
		7	1	6				
	3	2		4	7			
6	4				9		8	
	5	8		7	3			
	7				8			
1	5						3	9
2		6		3		5		1

Fill in each of the blank squares with the numbers 1 to 9, so that each row, each column and each 3x3 cell contains all the numbers from 1 to 9.

Turn To Page 172 For Solutions

Word Wheel

You have ten minutes to find as many words as possible using the letters in the wheel. Each word must be three letters or more and contain the central letter. Use each letter once and no plurals, foreign words or porper nouns are allowed. There is at least one nine-letter word.

The Extra

Fiction and reality collide as Sophie's life becomes cast in a new light...

By Lisa Allen

The sun rose like a golden film reel over Clegdon Hall. Marquees, trailers and catering vans littered a grassy field, equipment and crew crunched up the tree-lined drive, and from a high window squashed in the attic roof an excited face peered out.

Sophie couldn't believe her luck that *Summer At Kelly's* was actually going to be made into a movie – and filmed in her place of work.

It was her favourite historical novel, set in the 1930s, following a strong young woman called Helena, and her friends, through a summer of adventure and love.

It was romantic and funny, steeped in 1930s history – all the things that swept Sophie away.

How fortunate, of all the grand houses the location scout could have used, they chose Clegdon Hall, where Sophie worked as a house guide. She'd always secretly dreamed of being in a period drama; watching one being filmed was probably the closest she'd ever actually get to achieving that dream.

The house would be closed to the public for several weeks. But Sophie and other visitor experience staff had been asked to be on hand, guiding cast and crew to various parts of the estate during filming.

"Sophie?"

Sophie peeled her gaze away from the window. A skeleton crew of house staff were huddled at a small table in the attic offices, nursing mugs of steaming coffee.

"Sorry," replied Sophie, "I just can't believe we get to see an actual film being made."

Excited murmurings rippled around the circle of staff.

Malcolm frowned. He was general manager of the Clegdon Estate and

had absolutely no interest in showbiz whatsoever.

"Frankly, it's all going to be rather an inconvenience, all these people milling around with their cameras and cables, dressed in majestic attire."

"They are paying a princely fee to hire the house and grounds," chuckled someone else.

"Hmm. Yes, that will go some way towards paying for the roof repairs," Malcolm conceded, "so I suppose I'll just have to bear it."

Sophie grinned. Malcolm could be such a grump sometimes, but really, under that waxed jacket and starched shirt of his, he was just a cuddly old bear.

"Right, well, you've all been given your itineraries and walkie-talkies for the day. Any problems," added Malcolm, the frown deepening, "I'll be hiding up here, away from it all."

By mid-morning, the driveway was a buzzing hive of industry. A camera operator wheeled past Sophie on a short train track, filming alongside an open-top car skidding up to Clegdon Hall's high doors. Production staff angled reflective white screens as the three lead ➔

characters – dressed in full '30s costume – jumped out over the sports car's doors.

"We've finally arrived, darlings!"

"I can't believe we have a whole summer ahead of us."

"And what a summer we shall make it, Helena!"

"Aaaand CUT! OK, take five, everyone. Next shoot is inside the house, scene thirty-seven."

Sophie gazed dreamily ahead. She could feel a magic in the air she'd never experienced before; the world slipping

He grinned, gesturing to a full table in the corner of the marquee.

"We don't have time to queue up at the van, unfortunately. We've got to be back on set in ten minutes."

Sophie nodded, handing him the tray. "I feel very lucky getting to watch the process from behind the scenes.

"It's my favourite book, you know. I love Helena's story and how she…"

Her cheeks blotted pink; she was over-sharing with this handsome stranger.

He smiled. "Well now I definitely know

She could feel a magic in the air she'd never experienced before

between reality and fiction before her very eyes as the cast exited the set and made their way towards the ultra-modern catering vans.

She followed them over to the green room marquee, adjacent to the vans. It was time to swap with Jenny.

"Ooh, smells delicious." Sophie's eyes sparkled hungrily as Jenny handed her a tray of bacon rolls to offer out.

"Doesn't it?" said Jenny. "We're in the wrong job. Malcolm can barely bring himself to offer us one of his stale biscuits in the staff meetings, the mean old goat.

"Right, well that's me done. I'm guiding some crew down to the lake now."

"Have fun!"

"Excuse me."

Sophie spun round. A man, about her age, beanie hat slouched low over loose curls of short hair and trendy black glasses, smiled at her. He nodded at the tray of bacon rolls.

"Any chance these are going spare?"

Sophie grinned.

"Wow, filmmaking must be hungrier work than I first thought."

"They're not all for me, I promise."

who to talk to if any of my scenes aren't working. I'm afraid I've only read the script." He glanced over his shoulder.

"Listen, I better get this food to the hangry horde over there, but hopefully we'll bump into each other again."

Sophie nodded, her heart fluttering after him like a 1930s butterfly in full swoon.

H ey, sorry I had to rush off before. I didn't catch your name."

Sophie turned, her face lighting up at the sight of the handsome stranger from earlier approaching. "It's Sophie."

"Brian. I'm one of the assistant directors. How's it going?"

Sophie smiled. She was tucked behind a horseshoe of cameras, lighting, and production crew in the library.

They'd just been filming one of Sophie's favourite scenes from the novel.

"They performed it wonderfully – almost exactly as I'd visualised the scene when I read the book."

Brian grinned.

"We must be doing something right. Have you had film crews here before?"

Sophie shook her head.

"I wish! It's so exciting to watch."

"Sorry to interrupt." An older woman wearing a headset appeared beside them.

"But one of the extras in the next scene has just been called away. So, we're down a key extra."

Brian's face pinched. "OK, that leaves us with somewhat of a problem. We can't have any extras from the ballroom scene reappearing as a different extra in the garden party scene – eagle-eyed viewers always spot these things. Is there no one else?"

Hanna shook her head.

"I rang the talent agency; no one's available at such short notice."

Brian glanced at Sophie, an idea forming in his mind. "Sophie," he smiled, "ever fancied being in a film?"

Sophie's eyes widened. "What, me? I'm not a trained performer."

"But you'd be perfect," cajoled Brian, hypnotising her with his winning smile.

"Hanna – who are we looking for?"

Hanna grinned.

"Female, between twenty-five and thirty-five, has a sparkle in her eye."

Brian splayed his hands. "Hello! Right in front of us. And being a house guide takes a lot of confidence and excellent memory – that's a form of performing, isn't it?"

Sophie had never really thought of her job that way before. She just felt lucky to work somewhere she could share her enthusiasm and knowledge of the house with other people.

"All you'd really be doing is standing in the background with the other extras pretending to enjoy yourself at a raucous garden party," said Hanna.

"You wouldn't have any lines to say. It would be lots of fun!"

Brian smiled. "And didn't you tell me

earlier this is your favourite book? Now you'd get to be in it."

"But what if I'm terrible?"

"Don't worry. That's why we have a cutting room floor. If your acting is that bad, we'll just edit you out," laughed Hanna.

"You really think I could do it?"

Brian's eyes twinkled.

"Absolutely, and you'd be doing us a massive favour. Please?"

Sophie laughed. "OK, I'm in. I just really hope I don't embarrass myself!"

You've got the perfect look for a period drama," said Liz, dusting her make-up magic over Sophie's face. ➡

"We'll have to be careful you don't outshine the leading lady!"

Sophie giggled, staring in the mirror at her reflection. "I hardly recognise myself – it's like I've landed in actual 1932!"

Liz spritzed one last cloud of hairspray, smiling.

"I think you're ready for Costume now, my love. Just pop next door and Hanna will take you up to the garden set."

"That's supposed to be my job as house guide," said Sophie, grinning.

Liz winked at her in the mirror, laughing. "That can wait 'til tomorrow, hon. Today, you're a film star!"

Wow, look at you!"
Sophie blushed as Brian wandered towards her with script papers clutched in his hand. "I look the part maybe, but not sure if I feel the part yet."

Glancing around the garden, her stomach swirled with nerves. They'd cordoned off a section for the garden party scene, dressing it with picnic blankets, hampers and pretty parasols.

He grinned. "Ever heard that old saying, 'fake it til you make it'?"

Sophie laughed. "Does it work?"

His eyes crinkled. "Not sure. But nothing makes me feel as happy as when I'm on set, everyone having fun and working to create an imaginary world that one day thousands of people will sit down and enjoy escaping to."

Sophie had the same feeling when she was guiding visitors round Clegdon Hall or escaping into an old novel.

"Are you ready for your big moment?" Hanna called across.

Sophie looked at Brian, and he comfortingly touched her shoulder.

"You've got this."

She smiled; excitement and nerves fizzing in her chest.

Hanna guided Sophie to her spot among the other extras in the garden party scene, also giving her a reassuring smile. "Break a leg, as we say in the biz!"

The leading actors took their positions around the picnic, one flicking on the gramophone record.

Sophie felt her nerves fading away as she laughed and danced with the extras

A gramophone was being set up next to a huddle of other film extras, all dressed up like Sophie. It was all starting to feel strangely real now.

Panic started rising through her chest into her face. What if she made a fool of herself in front of all these professionals?

Brian looked at her, his eyes full of reassurance. "Can I let you in on a secret? This is my first film as assistant director, so I get how nervous you're probably feeling right now. Believe me, I've been feeling really nervous all day too."

Sophie's jaw dropped. "But you seem so confident?"

"Aaaand, take one!" The clapperboard snapped.

The lights shone as bright as the sun.

The cameras started rolling, and Sophie felt her nerves fading away as she laughed and danced with the other extras to the gramophone's scratchy melody.

She was Isobel – extra number fifteen – and she really did feel like a 1930s socialite that had sprung to life from the pages of her favourite book. The world of reality and fiction had collided.

And for a few wonderful minutes that she would remember for the rest of her life, Sophie's dream finally came true. Ⓜ

Brain Boosters

Codeword

Each letter of the alphabet has been replaced by a number. The numbers for the first name of our pictured celebrity are given. Work out which number represents which letter in the grid to reveal which TV game show Rylan Clark-Neal presented.

2	18	6	10	10	2	13	6	5	2	11		13	26	9
23		14		6		1		2		6		2		15
2	18	6	14	7		7	17	6	10	15	2	5	5	24
25		19		17		22			8		24		13
5	15	24	13	7	5		26	17	5	24	26	16	6	8
	16								6		1		17
17	6	10	6	16						12	2	5	26
2													26
16	6	24	8						20	6	7	24	8
22		16		1							5		
16	24	25	22	16	6	14	2		15	26	8	24	2	13 **R**
24		24		7			14		17		14		4 **Y**
12	24	7	1	6	8	24	7	2		2	3	1	6	8 **L**
2		26		21		14		14		13		8		6 **A**
7	24	13		2	18	17	8	26	13	6	5	24	26	16 **N**

A B C D E F G H I J K L M N O P Q R S T U V W X Y Z

1	2	3	4 **Y**	5	6 **A**	7	8 **L**	9	10	11	12	13 **R**
14	15	16 **N**	17	18	19	20	21	22	23	24	25	26

7	1	17	2	13 **R**	14	6 **A**	13 **R**	22	2	5		7	9	2	2	17

Turn To Page 172 For Solutions

Cherry Bakewell Traybake

Ingredients (Makes 15 squares)

- 150g plain flour
- Pinch of salt
- 30g white vegetable fat (Trex)
- 45g butter, chilled

For the filling:

- 2tbsp raspberry jam
- 50g glacé cherries, halved
- 100g butter, softened
- 100g caster sugar
- 2 eggs, beaten
- 125g ground almonds
- 125g plain cake crumbs
- Few drops almond essence

For the decoration:

- 25g glacé cherries, halved
- 25g toasted flaked almonds
- 50g icing sugar

1 Make the pastry. Sift the flour and salt into a mixing bowl and rub in the vegetable fat and butter to resemble breadcrumbs. Add 1-2tbsp chilled water to make a soft, but not sticky dough. Roll out on a lightly floured surface and use to line a 30 x 20cm baking tin. Chill.

2 Preheat the oven to 200°C, fan 180°C, Gas Mark 6. Spread the jam over the base of the tart and top with the glacé cherries.

3 Beat the butter and sugar together until light and creamy, then beat in the eggs. Add the ground almonds, cake crumbs and almond essence, stirring until mixed. Spread over the base.

4 Bake for 10 minutes, then reduce the temperature to 180°C, fan 160°C, Gas Mark 4 and bake for a further 15-20 minutes, until firm and golden. Cool completely.

5 Sprinkle the cherries and almonds over the tart. Mix the icing sugar with a little cold water and drizzle over the top. Leave to set. Cut into squares.

RECIPE AND FOOD STYLING: SUE ASHWORTH PHOTOGRAPHY: JONATHAN SHORT

Missing Link

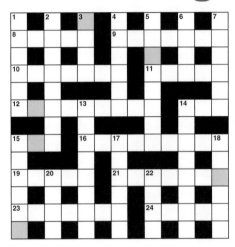

The answer to each clue is a word which has a link with each of the three words listed. This word may come at the end (eg **HEAD** linked with BEACH, BIG, HAMMER), at the beginning (eg **BLACK** linked with BEAUTY, BOARD and JACK) or a mixture of the two (eg **STONE** linked with HAIL, LIME and WALL).

ACROSS

8 Bill, Tea, Wooden (5)
9 Late, New, On (7)
10 President, Representative, To (7)
11 Coal, Gold, Tin (5)
12 Dangerous, Historical, Legal (9)
14 Brazil, Cutlet, Monkey (3)
15 Out, Over, Up (3)
16 Board, Economic, Speed (9)
19 Lane, Life, Spin (5)
21 Income, Moral, Technical (7)
23 Charge, Health, Self (7)
24 Dry, Spring, Sweep (5)

DOWN

1 Fall, Fast, Sound (6)
2 Art, Mass, Symphonic (8)
3 Garden, Granny, Slip (4)
4 Doggy, Steamer, Wheel (6)
5 Irony, Monologue, Tension (8)
6 Baked, Gas, Gloves (4)
7 Broccoli, Cauliflower, Silk (6)
13 Flu, Measles, Proportions (8)
14 Dioxide, Gas, Liquid (8)
15 Feeble, Good, Oneself (6)
17 Crop, Feather, Knuckle (6)
18 Credit, Customer, Naval (6)
20 Apple, Horse, Wheel (4)
22 Horse, Six, Welcome (4)

Turn To Page 172 For Solutions

Hidden word in the shaded squares: _____

Kriss Kross

Try to fit all of the listed words back into the grid.

4 letters	MAGMA	SPLURGE	10 letters
POLL	6 letters	8 letters	AMANUENSIS
REEF	FUNNEL	GRADUATE	RESTAURANT
SPIT	VIRAGO	STUNTMAN	11 letters
5 letters	7 letters	9 letters	COMFORTABLE
ALERT	AMATEUR	GUARANTOR	CONFINEMENT
EAGLE	SNAGGLE	LEYLANDII	

Turn To Page 172 For Solutions

Would It Be A Mistake?

A letter brings back memories of her teens – but had she achieved the hopes and dreams of her younger self?

By Glynis Scrivens

Finding the diary she'd written when she was fifteen, Christine forgot about decluttering and sat down to read it.

What struck her was the immediacy of the words. And their impact on her, even now. The day her crush turned up at her place unannounced. She'd looked up and he'd been standing in the open doorway.

Her feelings when she saw him sitting in a corner kissing Lynda at someone's birthday party a few weeks later.

Some of these memories had remained vivid and intense, instantly released by the words. How could all this have happened twenty years ago?

She flicked through the pages, trying not to read every sentence, but constantly lured back.

hopes of her fifteen-year-old self? But of course she had to read it, even knowing in advance that she'd fallen short of her own expectations and dreams.

Now that her own daughter's fifteenth birthday was approaching, it felt especially relevant. Would Kaylee compile a list of her own, she wondered?

She often felt that she didn't meet Kaylee's idea of a perfect mother.

Mind you, the concept of being a perfect mother had flown out the door two-and-a-half years ago, along with much else. Life as a single mother had been a matter of survival, not the pursuit of perfection.

Without realising it, she held her breath as she began to read the list in her diary.

The first item, predictably, was that she'd be Mrs Michael Peterson, living

Life as a single mother has been a matter of survival, not the pursuit of perfection

And then she found the list. "What I want my life to look like when I'm thirty," she'd written. She had no idea why she'd decided to make this list. Had she seen something like it in a movie? Had a girlfriend been compiling one?

Christine paused. Would it be a mistake to read this? To judge her thirty-five-year-old self by the thoughts and

in an old house with a big garden, and having a son or daughter.

She almost laughed. Kaylee was Michael's daughter, after all, and her home was certainly old. And when she was thirty, she and Michael had still been together. Not married, though.

They'd had their ups and downs over the years, separating and then making up

again. That is, until two years ago, when he'd simply moved to Italy and bought a stone house for next to nothing in a small southern village.

Judging by the photos, it looked like a lifetime's project. All because of an article he'd read in the weekend newspaper.

She still found it hard to believe. What had induced him to offer his services on an organic farm in a place neither of them had ever heard of?

In return, he was provided with accommodation and all his meals.

"It's only for three months," he'd said, when she protested.

To her surprise, Kaylee hadn't ➤

offered any resistance. At twelve, her daughter had thought his idea was cool.

"I'll do that when I'm an adult, too," she'd told Christine.

"I'll learn how to make wine, bake my own bread and grow olives."

Put in those terms, it certainly sounded enticing.

"You might even be able to work on the same farm where I'm going," Michael had said. "These farms stay in the same family for hundreds of years. I bet it'll even be there when your grandchildren are ready for an adventure."

Ready for an adventure. Christine understood that. But not the timing. This could've been an adventure the three of them could've had together, if Michael hadn't been so impulsive.

a Saturday job at the local supermarket to save up for a holiday in Italy with him.

Christine herself had refused to fly over. Michael had made a choice, she reasoned. And he'd done it without referring to her.

He denied that he'd left her, seeing it as a necessary separation in order for him to fulfil his dreams. All very well for him, but where did that leave her and Kaylee?

Christine bit her lip thoughtfully. Michael's invitation last week had come out of the blue. A postcard had arrived, his handwriting unmistakeable. How many times had she read it? The words refused to sink in.

Michael's stone house now had reliable plumbing, and a good-sized spare bedroom. Would Christine and Kaylee

Michael was always impulsive, but she could never have anticipated this

He only thought of himself and his own need for self-realisation.

He'd spent the entire summer there, posting images on social media of sun-drenched landscapes, impossibly blue seas and grape vines.

Then came the bombshell she could never have seen coming: buying a place of his own in the village. For next to nothing.

"I'll get it ready for us," he'd said, without giving any serious thought to the impact this would have on her and Kaylee.

He'd continued working on the farm, using it as a base while he began the slow resurrection of the stone cottage.

Michael was always impulsive. But she'd never anticipated anything like this could happen.

Now and again, he flew back to Dorset to visit his ageing parents, and she'd catch up with him. And he constantly kept in touch on social media. Kaylee had taken

like to fly out to visit him and stay a week or two? He could pick them up from the airport in Rome.

The village had a bustling seafood market, a piazza boasting numerous cafes and ristorantes, and the sparkling blue Mediterranean was a mere fifteen-minute drive away through vineyards and olive groves.

In her heart Christine was ready to hop on the next plane. But how would she feel once she was there? And how would she cope if Kaylee wanted to stay for an extended period once she'd flown home again?

Was Michael involved in an intimate relationship? He hadn't mentioned anyone and she hadn't felt she could ask. Nor had she volunteered any information about her own love life, non-existent though it was. Until now, she'd been able to keep their relationship in a separate

at everything through the prism of Michael's new life. Part of her felt excited, another part was scared.

Then there was the cost. Air fares weren't cheap. If she was flying to Italy for her annual holiday, why restrict herself to one village? Michael had offered to pick them up in Rome, but she felt tempted to fly to Milan, hire a car and then leisurely drive south, spending time in Florence and Rome, while also taking in some of the lovely old towns like Positano. Maybe Naples, too?

Michael was there, doing his own thing. She'd like to do her own thing, too.

Would Kaylee agree? Surely any twelve-year-old would leap at the opportunity? Christine would meet their extra travelling costs, naturally.

Two weeks passed without her knowing how to reply to Michael's invitation. She hadn't resolved the issue of where to stay. Not entirely. She knew Kaylee would stay in Michael's stone house. But was that what she herself wanted? Would she share a bed with him?

Clearly, he seemed to think nothing fundamental had changed between them. That he'd simply pioneered the way for a different kind of future together. But that's not how it felt to her.

She couldn't blame him, either. When he'd flown over last Christmas, she'd forgotten her resolves and they'd spent a night together.

Patting the postcard which she kept in her jeans pocket, she continued reading the list her fifteen-year-old self had compiled.

Item two was to have an interesting job. "One where I'm never bored," she'd written.

Never bored? She'd certainly set her sights high. But she was satisfied she'd found her life's work. Christine was a psychologist. ➡

compartment in her life. She'd seen Michael several times a year, each time for a few days, and always somewhere neutral like his parents' farm or a café.

Never in her home where inevitably his presence and memories would linger after he'd left. And just as inevitably, she'd be tempted to go to bed with him.

Keeping him at arm's length was how she'd dealt with everything.

How would she cope going to visit him?

Living in the same house for a week or two would be an altogether different experience; one that'd leave her feeling vulnerable.

But, of course, she knew they'd catch that plane. That they'd be in Italy looking

She smiled as a thought crossed her mind. She pictured herself in a session with a fellow psychologist, explaining the dilemmas she faced in her on-again off-again relationship with Michael. What advice would someone neutral give her? What advice would she herself offer to someone in that situation?

And what questions would she ask?

What do you want from this relationship? What kind of future do you feel is possible when one partner is free to pursue any path that beckons? Are there unfulfilled dreams of your own that've lain dormant while Michael is pursuing his?

What would life look like if you made a clean break from this relationship? Have

mantra in life. Unmarried. Feeling free to wander the globe, unfettered by parenthood.

Or was he more perceptive than her? More at ease in his skin? More in tune with his hopes and dreams?

Christine closed her diary. Her decision was made. Yes, she and Kaylee would travel to Italy. There were places she wanted to explore and experience.

Staying with Michael would be an important part of this holiday. But she couldn't afford to let it be everything.

Not until the unlikely circumstance that he changed and gave weight to what she and Kaylee wanted, rather than just listening to his own desires.

There was only one more item on her teenage list. Don't be tied down

you considered the possibility of moving to Italy for twelve months? By the end of a year, you'd know in your heart whether or not you wanted to remain – both in Italy and with Michael.

She bit her lip. Michael hadn't suggested they stay that long, just a week or two. Did that suggest a lack of longer-term commitment on his part? Or was he simply being pragmatic? The visit would coincide with Kaylee's school holidays.

There was only one more item on her teenage list.

Don't be tied down.

That could be on a wish list compiled by Michael. Why had she written that? How was it consistent with owning an old house with a big garden?

Of course, she'd been fifteen when she'd written this, wanting her sense of freedom to last forever.

Has Michael ever grown up? she asked herself.

Don't be tied down was his unwritten

She'd sleep in his spare bedroom with Kaylee, on a mattress on the floor if necessary.

For the first time in days, she felt something resembling peace.

What if she, too, found a house she fell in love with?

Don't be tied down she'd written. That applied to both England and Italy. It'd be easy to let out her home in Dorset if the occasion arose.

The rent would allow her to live well in an Italian village. Not necessarily the same village as Michael.

A pipe dream? Probably. But she'd reached a time in her life where she wanted to keep open the windows of possibility.

The Italian adventure could be a learning experience for both herself and Kaylee.

After all, the aspirations and feelings of two fifteen-year-old girls needed to be taken into account. ⓜ

Brain Boosters

Sudoku

							5	
	2	8			4		3	9
	7		5			2		
8		1	2	9			7	
	5	9			6			
					8	4		
			7	1		2		
7				6		9	1	
	8				3			

Fill in each of the blank squares with the numbers 1 to 9, so that each row, each column and each 3x3 cell contains all the numbers from 1 to 9.

Turn To Page 172 For Solutions

Word Wheel

You have ten minutes to find as many words as possible using the letters in the wheel. Each word must be three letters or more and contain the central letter. Use each letter once and no plurals, foreign words or porper nouns are allowed. There is at least one nine-letter word.

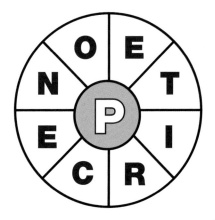

Over The Hill

Their families may have been sceptical, but these ladies weren't prepared to stay at a loose end for long...

By Jan Snook

Next month she'd be seventy-two, Jean thought irritably, as she looked out at the dreary January morning. Things were definitely going downhill. Where had the last year gone?

The whole family would be coming for lunch on her birthday, and she now wished, of course, that she hadn't been so pig-headed as to insist that they come to her. But when her daughters had suggested – weeks ago – that lunch for ten of them would be too much for her, Jean's hackles had risen and she'd proclaimed herself to be "not quite over the hill yet, thank you very much".

"Which means, of course," Jean complained to her friend Veronica over a cup of coffee a day or two after this arrangement had been made, "that I'll have to go to more trouble than usual, just to prove that I can!"

"But you always go to a lot of trouble,"

Veronica said loyally.

"Well, I try," Jean agreed, "but Christa's wretched husband Richard…"

"What's he done now?"

"He made some supercilious remark along the lines of 'don't worry, something easy like roast chicken and stewed fruit will be fine'!"

"Oh, dear," Veronica said, smiling. "Red rag to a bull, I imagine."

"As you say. He means well, but somehow always says the wrong thing."

Veronica raised her eyebrows.

"So now?"

"Oh, well, now I'm planning Stilton and almond biscuits with drinks, and stuffed loin of pork with ratatouille and boulangère potatoes, and then a French apple flan…"

"It all sounds absolutely delicious, so why are you still looking worried?"

Jean said nothing for a moment, but sipped her coffee then sighed.

"Well, it's nearly a year since Bill died, and they – the girls, I mean – are beginning to intimate that I should be socialising again…"

"But there's our book group and bridge club and…" Veronica tailed off, then looked miserable.

"I do know what you mean, though. It was the same after Jim died. Simon and Alicia kept asking me to go to Ibiza with them, or join a quilting group."

"Oh, yes, I remember the holiday invitations. They would have been out clubbing every night, and you would have been babysitting." ➤

"And making sandcastles all day. Don't get me wrong, I love my grandchildren dearly, but entertaining little tots isn't exactly a holiday, it's hard work."

"Absolutely," Jean agreed. "Been there, done that. What I need," she continued, "is a plan, so that when they suggest I join a crochet club or something, I can say 'well no, I'm doing such-and-such'…"

"A few friends have said similar things recently," Veronica said thoughtfully.

"There are clearly a lot of us about. Let's think."

"You? Paddle boarding?" Ella said faintly. "In February?"

The entire family (except for her youngest grandchild, eight-year-old Barney) had their mouths open.

"What's wrong with paddle boarding?" he asked. "Did you fall in?" he added enthusiastically.

"As it happens, I did," Jean smiled, "and so did Veronica."

"You could have caught your death, Mum," Ella protested.

"For heaven's sake, it's February! We weren't wearing bikinis! We had wetsuits

"Entertaining little tots isn't exactly a holiday, it's hard work"

The day of Jean's birthday dawned, and she found she had rather more cards than usual – many of them from her new friends in the recently-formed Nothing Up Club.

One of the rules they'd made at the first meeting was that birthday cards should make you laugh: tasteful pictures of flowers were old-ladyish and should be avoided if at all possible.

"Who on earth sent you this one?" Ella, Jean's daughter, asked.

She didn't wait for an answer, however, but read the message inside, then exchanged dark looks with Christa.

"I'm sorry," Jean said as she handed round a bowl of olives (though not sounding remotely apologetic).

"I meant to make some of those Stilton and almond biscuits you all like, but I've had a really busy couple of weeks."

"Oh, dear," Ella's partner said, looking concerned. "Hospital appointments?"

"Goodness, no. I went paddle boarding with the Nothing Up Club on Tuesday.

"It was great! We've decided to make it a regular event and–"

on! Anyway, the week before that we went to that dry ski slope. Not so sure about that, but I'll have another go. Someone's organising a skiing trip."

"Have you lost your senses, Mum? People break legs and things on ski trips!"

"Obviously we'll be starting on the nursery slopes," Jean replied tartly.

"And I'd remind you that ladies of my age break bones tripping over sweet wrappers – we might as well get injured doing something exciting!"

"What on earth would Dad say?" Christa asked, disapprovingly.

"He'd say 'Go, Girl!'" Barney replied, sounding so like his grandfather that everyone laughed.

At that moment, the phone rang.

"That'll be Veronica," Jean said happily, "to confirm the time of our self-defence classes. She's the president of the Nothing Up Club."

"Good name," Richard said. "Is it because you're all at a bit of a loose end?"

Jean pealed with laughter.

"Certainly not! It stands for Not Over The Hill – I'm Not Giving Up!" Ⓜ

Brain Boosters

Codeword

Each letter of the alphabet has been replaced by a number. The numbers for the first name of our pictured celebrity are given. Work out which number represents which letter in the grid to reveal in which crime drama Emilia Fox played Dr Nikki Alexander.

A B C D E F G H I/J K L M N O P Q R S T U V W X Y Z

1	2	3	4	5	6	7 I	8	9	10	11	12 E	13
14 L	15	16	17	18	19	20 A	21 M	22	23	24	25	26

10	7	14 L	12 E	6	16		9	7	16	6	12 E	10	10
			I					I					

Turn To Page 173 For Solutions

Smoky Haddock And Spinach Pancakes

Ingredients (Serves 4)

◆ 110g plain flour
◆ Pinch of salt
◆ 1 egg
◆ 275ml skimmed milk
◆ Few drops of vegetable oil
◆ 200g smoked haddock
◆ 150g young spinach
◆ 100g mature Cheddar cheese, grated
◆ 4tbsp fromage frais
◆ Cherry tomatoes and parsley, to serve

1 Preheat oven to 190°C, fan 170°C, Gas 5. Sift the flour and salt into a large jug or mixing bowl. Add the egg and milk and beat with a wire whisk to make a smooth batter.

2 Heat a few drops of oil in a pancake pan or non-stick frying pan. Pour in a thin stream of batter, tilting the pan so that it flows evenly across the surface. Cook over a medium heat until the surface sets, then flip the pancake over to cook the other side. Make 4 pancakes in total, adding a few drops of oil before cooking each one.

3 Put the haddock in a frying pan and cover with boiling water. Simmer gently for 4-5 minutes until cooked, when the flesh will flake easily. Drain well and flake into large chunks. At the same time, cook the spinach in a little water until the leaves wilt, 3-4 minutes. Drain well, squeezing out the excess moisture with the back of a spoon.

4 Sprinkle half the cheese over the pancakes. Arrange an equal amount of fish and spinach on top. Spoon on the fromage frais. Fold into triangles, place in a baking dish, or individual dishes, and sprinkle with the rest of the cheese.

5 Heat in the oven for 15-20 minutes. Serve with cherry tomatoes and parsley.

RECIPE AND FOOD STYLING: SUE ASHWORTH PHOTOGRAPHY: JONATHAN SHORT

Wedding Surprise

Would Carrie ever measure up to her son's expectations – or had she ruined his special day?

By Tess Niland Kimber

"One job, Mum," Lewis shouted, storming out of the kitchen. "That's all, but you've messed up – big time!"

Carrie flinched waiting for the inevitable door slam. It came and she closed her eyes, trying to stem the equally inevitable tears. Her husband Steve put out a steadying hand.

"Leave him, Carrie. He's better on his own when he's like this."

"But Lewis is right," she sobbed. "All I had to do was organise the passports. And I couldn't even do that."

Steve pulled her into his arms.

"Emotions always get heightened at weddings, you know that.

"The slightest problem and it kicks off."

Carrie had been looking forward to the wedding. Phoebe and Lewis were holding the ceremony on an Italian beach near Sorrento where his dad, Nathan, lived with his new wife, Sofia.

"You alright with that, Mum?" Lewis had asked when they'd revealed the wedding venue.

"Sure – you know Dad and I still get on. And it's a good excuse for a holiday." She'd checked in with Steve then, but he'd looked totally cool with the idea.

"All that sun and limoncello – what's not to like? Just check our passports. Make sure they've not expired," Steve cautioned as they'd opened a bottle of champagne to celebrate.

"I will, but I'm pretty certain we don't have to renew for a year."

"All that sun and limoncello – what's not to like? Just check our passports"

She looked up at him.

"But that's not all it is, is it? Me and Lewis have always… struggled to get on. We're not like you and your two boys."

"Trust me," Steve said, curling his arms around her. "Once the wedding's over, things'll calm down."

"You think so?"

He kissed the tip of her nose.

"I know so."

"Well, best make sure, Mum," Lewis had held her gaze with his brown eyes.

She agreed, but the idea was soon forgotten as they chatted through options for flowers and food and discussed which family and friends might join them.

As the date neared, Lewis became stressed. Carrie noticed he'd snap at the slightest thing and their ➡

already fragile relationship suffered.

"Don't take any notice, love," Steve would caution. "He's under pressure."

"I know, but it's hard to take. It reminds me of when Nathan and I split. When Lewis really played up."

Although Carrie and Nathan had tried their best to soften the blow of the divorce, Lewis, then in his early teens, had briefly gone off the rails. Nothing major, but their relationship had soured as Carrie had taken on more work, often leaving Lewis on his own.

Nathan had been as generous as he could afford, but he'd moved to Italy not long after the divorce. Keen for Lewis to visit his dad as often as possible, Carrie had taken on an evening job, in addition to her child-minding business, to help pay for air tickets and the extra costs of running the home alone.

"Do you have to go out – again?" Lewis would complain when she slipped on her overalls to clean the offices.

"Sorry, darling, but we need the money," she'd tell him.

He clearly resented her absence and his behaviour deteriorated. He was cheeky and disobedient at home. Then the school complained about missing homework and the standard of his classwork.

"I don't know what's wrong with you, lately," Carrie would say, as she rushed out on another cleaning job.

"There's nothing wrong with me – it's you!" he'd argue. "You've got more time for the kids that you look after than you have for me."

"That's not true!" she'd argue, feeling upset as she left the house.

How she longed for the little boy she'd once cherished to return.

When he was caught trespassing with his new friends and was cautioned by the police, Carrie was mortified.

Nathan was just as cross, but from that day on, Lewis started to behave again.

"I think the police frightened him as much as they did us," Nathan said to Carrie.

Although Lewis's behaviour improved, the warmth they'd once shared didn't return. It made Carrie sad, but she threw herself into her business, working long hours to muffle her blues.

Having babies and toddlers to care for filled some of the Lewis-shaped gap, but she still longed for their old closeness.

"I don't know how you do it," one dad told her. "I find it hard enough just looking after my two."

Steve Parkin, recently divorced, had enrolled his sons with her.

"I love it. The more the merrier. I'm one of seven."

"Wow!" Steve had said. "Do you have a big family of your own?"

"No – just one boy. Nathan and I split before we could have more children."

"That's a shame," he'd said.

"Well, these little ones are like my extended family, so I haven't missed out."

She didn't like to admit to Steve that she felt a failure as a mum. Over the next few months, she and the tall, grey-haired man often made time for a coffee when he dropped off the boys.

She liked him. He was a builder and shared custody of eight-year-old Benjy and five-year-old Max with his ex-wife.

That summer, Carrie employed Steve to change the dining room into a playroom to accommodate her growing business. While the work was carried out, they grew closer.

"Let me treat you to dinner – to thank you," she'd said when the stunning new room was finished.

Over tapas and a bottle of Rioja in Solera's restaurant, they'd fallen in love.

By the time Lewis left school, Carrie

had married Steve. Luckily, the two men in her life bonded, and Lewis accepted an apprenticeship at Steve's building firm.

"He's a really good worker," Steve told her approvingly. "Got quite a flair for bricklaying, too."

Tentatively, Carrie began to hope that the bad years were behind them, and when Lewis met Phoebe he really seemed to have settled down.

Phoebe Atkins brought a breath of fresh air into the Parkin household. She was lively, fun – and what's more, she sought out Carrie's company.

"It's great to have someone to go shopping with or chat over the soaps," she'd tell Steve.

"It must be, love," he said warmly.

"Wow! That's great, just what Phoebe would wear. Thanks, Mum, you're a star."

Carrie was so thrilled that she could have danced in the shopping centre, but that really would've annoyed Lewis!

When Lewis and Phoebe announced their engagement, Carrie was delighted. Although they were quite young, they were committed to making their relationship work.

"I want to give Phoebe the best day ever," Lewis had confided in Carrie.

She'd smiled, delighted her son was so in love. As the wedding plans took shape, Lewis surprised them by suggesting they hold the ceremony on a beach in Italy, near to Nathan and Sofia's home.

"I want to give Phoebe the best day ever," Lewis confided in Carrie

"And she certainly manages to bring out the best in Lewis."

Lewis had enrolled in an online architecture course and last week he'd told Steve he was too busy to go fishing as he was revising.

"Gosh, I need to sit down," she joked. "Lewis revising!"

Subtly Phoebe brought Carrie and Lewis closer, drawing her into conversations or including Carrie and Steve in their plans. When it was Phoebe's birthday, Lewis shocked Carrie by asking her to help him choose a present.

Her heart sung as they wandered the shopping mall looking for something special. How good it felt to spend time like this with her son.

Looking in the window of Randall's Jewellers she spotted a beautiful silver bangle – a slim coil, entwined by two metal raindrops. Hesitantly, she suggested it to him.

"We can honeymoon there afterwards," Lewis had suggested.

It sounded great, and as Max and Benjy were to be pageboys, Steve and Carrie planned a family holiday in the area after the wedding.

But as the big day neared, Lewis became more stressed. Carrie saw flashes of the old teenager who'd easily lose his temper. Only Phoebe was able to calm him.

Carrie took the brunt of his bad moods and began to wish the wedding was over. The beach venue had sounded relaxed, but arrangements became complex as Phoebe and Lewis wanted two receptions – one in Italy and another at home in England for friends and family who couldn't attend the actual ceremony.

Even shopping for an outfit filled Carrie with little enthusiasm. As the date drew near, she felt flat. ➡

"It'll be OK," Steve had soothed, rubbing her tense shoulders.

But nothing he said could cheer her. All she could think about was enjoying some holiday downtime after the wedding.

Everything came to a head when Carrie was packing and finally checked the passports.

"Steve, these should be renewed," she gasped, checking when they expired. "They're in date, but Phoebe said some countries like a year on them."

Lewis came home then, complaining that he was struggling to explain their floral needs to the Italian florist. Sensing the tension, he asked what was wrong.

"Mum thought the passports were in order, but Italy like at least three months before expiry. Carrie's only has two months left."

"One job, Mum," Lewis shouted, storming out of the kitchen. "That's all, but you've messed up – big time!"

Carrie was upset, but as Steve held her in his arms, he told her they could make an appointment and travel to the passport office in London.

"It'll be a pain, and more expensive, but we can renew the passports in one day when we're there."

Through her tears Carrie smiled, pleased there was a solution.

I can't believe we're on our way," Steve said, as the plane took off.

Carrie held his hand as she looked out of the window at the ground disappearing below.

"I'm looking forward to the holiday, especially with these two," she smiled at Benjy and Max who were now teenagers.

She closed her eyes, still feeling anxious. Since the passport issue, Lewis had been reserved around her. Steve had tried to dismiss it as more wedding nerves, but Carrie was secretly frightened that this latest road bump in their rocky mother-son relationship had caused irreparable damage.

Look at that sea!" Carrie said, leaning over the hotel balcony as they prepared to leave for the wedding, the warm breeze tangling her dark hair.

"It's beautiful, just like you," Steve said, handsome in a white shirt over oatmeal-coloured shorts.

"Thank you." Carrie smiled, pleased with the dark-blue halterneck dress she'd finally chosen.

The silky material was decorated with sand-coloured splashes and the neckline fastened by a silver choker. She only hoped Lewis would approve.

As Carrie, Steve, Max and Benjy walked the short distance to the beach for the ceremony, she bit her lip. She was nervous. Was there an unforeseen detail she'd forgotten that would ruin the day for Lewis and Phoebe?

Reaching the beach, they instantly spotted Lewis standing under an arch of pink bougainvillea, waiting for his bride. Barefoot, he looked incredibly handsome in a blue-grey linen suit.

As soon as he noticed them, he gave them a dazzling smile. Carrie felt tears pricking and she raised her hand in a small, tight wave.

"OK?" she mouthed.

He nodded, but rocked his hand to indicate his nerves.

"You'll be fine," she whispered back.

Before they took their seats, she gave Nathan and Sofia a welcoming hug.

Then it was time for Max and Benjy to take up their positions as Steve squeezed Carrie's hand.

"See, I said it would be OK."

"I'm almost beginning to believe you." She sighed with relief.

It was hopeless to try to stem the tears, Carrie thought, when Phoebe arrived, looking stunning in a white satin dress.

The ceremony was beautiful, set against the backdrop of the sapphire Tyrrhenian Sea and the drama of Vesuvius in the distance.

As Steve passed her yet another tissue, he whispered, "I hope they're happy tears."

"Oh yes," she smiled. "I'm just thinking what a long way Lewis has come and I'm delighted for him."

"He's done well, thanks to you. And if they're half as happy as us, they'll be absolutely fine."

After the heat of the Italian sun, Carrie was pleased and relieved that the reception was to be held in the cool of their hotel.

"You boys did us proud," she said to Max and Benjy, who beamed as they sat at the table.

Since the wedding was held abroad, the wedding party was quite small with just Phoebe's parents, her sister, the Parkin family, Lewis's best friend Joel

and Phoebe's two old school friends.

The hotel had laid on a stunning buffet of fish, chicken, salad, bread, olives, crostini and in the centre of the table was a traditional Italian wedding cake, a large millefoglie – layers of wafer-thin pastry covered in cream and fresh fruit.

"This is just amazing," Carrie breathed. "It makes me want to get married all over again."

Steve pretended to bury his head in his hands.

"I couldn't cope with the stress," he groaned. "Although I'd definitely marry ➡

you a hundred times over, my love."

Before she could answer, a shrill ring resonated as Phoebe's dad George tapped his wine glass and stood up; the speeches were about to begin.

"Well, thank you all for coming…" he started.

After George had made a brilliant speech welcoming him to the family, Lewis stood up.

"Wow! How can I follow that?" he said. "Firstly, I must thank everyone for coming all this way to celebrate our wedding with us. I want to thank my gorgeous bride for agreeing to marry me, Joel for his amazing job as best man – thank you for not losing the ring…"

As they laughed and the thank yous continued, Carrie began to feel nervous.

"We didn't have an awful lot of money when I was young, but by taking on extra work, Mum ensured I never went without.

"And what did I do? I gave her a hard time for it, but only because I missed her so much."

That was it for Carrie; tears poured down her face.

"So, I want to thank everyone – Phoebe, George and Sarah, Dad and Sofia, Benjy and Max, Steve, but most of all Mum. Please raise your glasses."

Steve passed Carrie a tissue as she wiped her eyes, barely able to lift her glass for the toast.

Thank you, Lewis, for those lovely words," Carrie said as they kissed the bride and groom goodbye. "I never knew you felt that way…"

For a moment Carrie was stunned. Had she heard him correctly?

She hoped against hope that he wouldn't mention the issue with the passport and how she'd let him down.

"I also want to thank my stepdad Steve for all his sound advice over the years and my dad and stepmum for helping us with the honeymoon."

As Carrie nodded her thanks to Nathan she almost missed Lewis's next words.

"And I've left the best 'til last, as I want to thank my amazing mum."

For a minute Carrie was stunned. Had she heard him correctly?

"It's no secret I was a bit of a handful when I was growing up and gave poor Mum a hard time. But she showed me the most wonderful example of how to be a better person, through hard work, patience and kindness."

Tears filled Carrie's eyes as she listened to her son's heartfelt accolade.

"Well, I stupidly didn't say it, did I? But I love you, Mum, always have and always will. You're the best," he said, hugging her tightly.

"Come on, you two, the taxi's waiting to take the bride and groom on honeymoon," Steve smiled, as mother and son reluctantly pulled apart.

As the wedding party waved off the happy couple, her son's words rang in Carrie's ears.

"You're the best…" Lewis had said.

And as she watched their taxi disappearing into the distance amid the rolling olive groves, she thought tenderly, *And you, my darling, precious son, are the very best I could ever have wished for, too.*

Out-of-date passports, slamming doors, and moody teenage exchanges… suddenly they all meant nothing at all. ⓂⓌ

Brain Boosters

Kriss Kross

Try to fit all of the listed words back into the grid.

4 letters
NEED
OAST
SAGO
WIDE

5 letters
TWANG
YOUTH

7 letters
AGELESS
LULLABY

8 letters
ADHESION
GLOAMING
LONESOME

9 letters
BLUEBERRY
FLASHBULB

10 letters
MARVELLOUS
PLIABILITY

11 letters
INDIVISIBLE
UNFURNISHED

Turn To Page 173 For Solutions

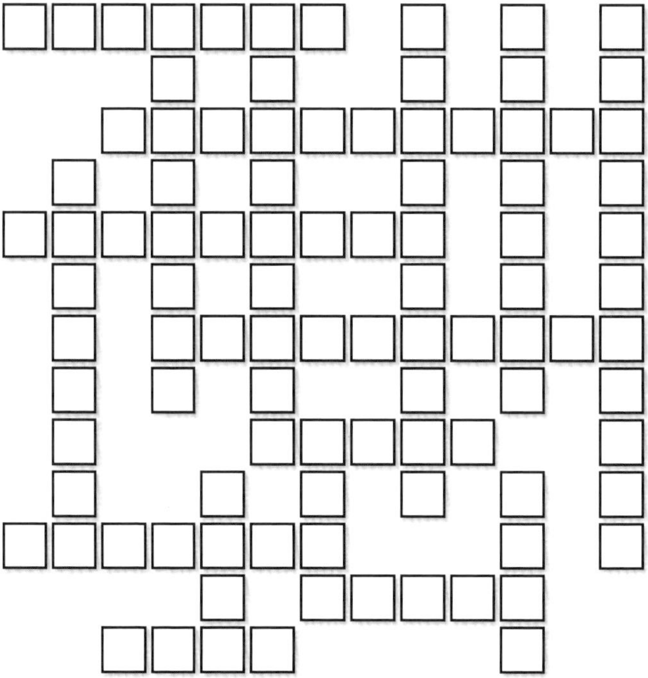

That's Life

His new hobby was drawing, but was it the art – or the subject matter – he was really interested in...?

By Gail Warrick Cox

I've signed up for an art class at the community centre on Thursday mornings," John announced as he bustled through the door loaded with shopping.

John was newly retired. Debbie had finished work a couple of years previously and was settled in a weekly routine of hobbies, clubs and socialising. She had suggested John join the local walking group, Wednesday's wild swimmers or the badminton club, but he had joked he already knew how to walk, swim and play badminton. That what he really wanted was to try something completely different, to learn a new skill.

was surprised John had signed up for it. She wouldn't have thought drawing scantily clad models was John's thing but, then, he had said he wanted to try something completely different.

"What made you choose that particular class?" Debbie asked.

"The lady at reception said it's a good one to start with. Apparently, it focuses on the observation of form." John recited exactly what the woman had told him.

"Hmm," Debbie said. "When do you start?"

"Next Thursday," he replied. "It's just for six weeks to learn the basics, see if you like it. And if you do, there are other courses to progress to."

She wouldn't have thought drawing scantily clad models was John's thing

"That's great, love," Debbie said with a smile. She was delighted John had chosen a hobby and actually committed to it.

He'd seemed a little lost since finishing work. She remembered her own transition into retirement and it had taken a bit of getting used to. She hoped the course would provide John with an interest, something to fill his time, somewhere he could meet people and learn something new.

"What sort of art course is it?" she asked.

"It's a life class for beginners," he told her.

Debbie didn't know much about art, but she knew what a life class was. She

He put the shopping bags on the kitchen counter.

"I'm going to pop back out now," he said. "Go to the art shop in town, see if I can pick up a large sketchpad and some different grades of pencils."

And with that, he was gone.

Debbie unpacked the groceries. She was pleased John was excited to start his new class, but she wasn't sure she felt completely comfortable with him "focusing on the observation of form", however innocent it was.

When Thursday came, John was up early. He'd showered, dressed and breakfasted by nine and was heading out the door by half past. Debbie noticed a

waft of aftershave as he passed her in the hall. He didn't normally wear any, just on special occasions. She watched him stroll down the drive, a backpack containing his pencils and pad slung over his shoulder, his usual parting peck on the cheek for her omitted today. He didn't even turn to wave goodbye. Perhaps he was nervous about starting something new and had overlooked their usual little rituals.

John arrived home just after one, clearly buoyed up by attending the class.

He was full of it: details of the tutor, the classroom, the other students and the quick coffee they had gone for after the lesson all spilling from his lips in animated waves of enthusiasm.

Debbie was pleased he had enjoyed himself. "What did you draw?" she asked.

"Oh, we didn't do much drawing," John replied. "The tutor just went over the basics today. Pencil types, perspective, light and shade, that sort of thing.

"We did a couple of quick sketches of items in the room but the real life drawing starts next week."

"Lovely," Debbie said, forcing a smile.

The following Thursday when John returned home, he was once again brimming with details of how the class had gone.

"We did our first proper drawing today," he said, his smile wide. "We had to focus on the subject, to look really ➤

carefully, take it all in, then replicate what we saw in real life on the paper."

Debbie bristled. "How did that go?"

"Great!" John beamed.

"The tutor said how well I'd managed to capture all the curves."

Debbie looked for the telltale blotches of embarrassment that would occasionally appear on John's cheeks, but there were none. Her forehead furrowed.

"Can I see your drawing?" she asked.

John pulled the sketchpad from his rucksack and opened it, smoothing the page and sliding it across the table for Debbie to look at.

She stared at his drawing in disbelief.

It was really good. The tutor was right, he had captured the curves beautifully, his technique of shading and smudging giving his work a realistic three-dimensional effect.

"It's fruit!" Debbie blurted out.

"A melon, grapes and peaches."

John's face contorted with confusion.

"What were you expecting?"

"I thought you were attending a life class."

"I am." John grinned, the misunderstanding between them becoming clear. "Still life!"

They broke into a fit of giggles. "Can you imagine me at an actual life class?" John chuckled. "I'd be so embarrassed."

"I know." Debbie smiled, and she kissed the red blotch forming on his cheek. Ⓜ

RECIPE AND FOOD STYLING: JENNIE SHAPTER   PHOTOGRAPHY: JON WHITAKER

Croissant Pudding

Ingredients (Serves 2)

- ◆ **2 large day-old croissants**
- ◆ **25g butter, softened**
- ◆ **25g dried apricots, chopped**
- ◆ **25g dried cranberries**
- ◆ **150ml milk**
- ◆ **100ml single cream**
- ◆ **2 eggs**
- ◆ **25g caster sugar**
- ◆ **Few drops vanilla essence**
- ◆ **2tsp demerara sugar**

1 Cut each croissant into 6 slices and spread one cut side with butter. Arrange, butter side up, in a 600ml ovenproof dish, scattering with apricots and cranberries.

2 Pour the milk and cream into a saucepan and warm. In a bowl, whisk the eggs, caster sugar and vanilla together. Whisk in the milk and cream. Pour over the croissants and leave to stand for 10 minutes.

3 Preheat the oven to 180°C, fan 160°C, Gas Mark 4.

4 Sprinkle the demerara sugar over the pudding and bake for 25-30 minutes, until golden and the custard is set. For a single serving, bake for 20 minutes. Serve warm.

Endless Summer

Joanne and her aunt each had a compelling personal reason to travel halfway round the world…

By Glynis Scrivens

Joanne had to read the email twice before she could believe it.

Why would Aunt Marilyn want to house swap and leave behind lazy days on her sun-soaked veranda overlooking the Brisbane River for Joanne's cramped flat in Malvern, where Septembers were invariably wet and miserable?

This was definitely the easiest decision she'd ever made.

Yet as she sat at her desk, raindrops rolling down the windowpanes, a seed of worry took root.

It was uncharacteristic of Aunt Marilyn to do anything at the last minute. She was a woman who did her Christmas shopping at the January sales.

So why had she written in August to ask whether Joanne could swap homes for four weeks from early September?

I can't leave my roses to the mercy of the weather and the brushturkeys, she'd

written. *Anthony will look after Forrest and the chickens until you arrive.*

Joanne remembered the gangly, anxious-to-please puppy. He must be huge now. And she certainly remembered Aunt Marilyn's neighbour.

Even as Joanne arrived at Gatwick for her flight a few weeks later, she was none the wiser.

It was hard not to feel excited when the plane began its descent towards Brisbane Airport. Looking out of the window, she marvelled as lavender baubles across the city slowly became flowering jacarandas. It looked as though an impressionist painter had been at work. Except for the river, which resembled a coiling brown snake. More like something John Constable might have painted.

She thought of Aunt Marilyn's neighbour. Anthony lived in the workers' cottage next door. His quarter-acre block was organised chaos. David Austin roses sat among cocos palms, huge tree ferns

and fuchsia-coloured bougainvillea, with Muscovy ducks and Pekin chickens free-ranging everywhere.

Aunt Marilyn was waiting at the luggage carousel. Behind her was Anthony looking just as rugged and athletic as she remembered. As their eyes met, he gave her a warm, crooked smile. She felt her knees melt, as they had done seven years ago. But Anthony was married with a daughter now.

Aunt Marilyn hugged her tightly.

"So wonderful to see you. And do you remember Anthony?"

"Of course," Joanne said, and found herself momentarily wrapped in his arms.

"Are you too tired for a little sightseeing?" he asked, as he wheeled her suitcase and cabin bag to his car.

"Perhaps another day?" Aunt Marilyn answered for her. "She's been cooped up in a plane for twenty-seven hours."

Joanne felt breathless from his hug, aware of their old chemistry.

Last time she was here there'd been

moments when they'd watched the sunset on the river or viewed the city from Mount Coot-Tha lookout, when the idea of simply staying in Australia had arisen.

Joanne couldn't help noticing that Anthony chose the scenic route to New Farm, detouring through jacaranda-lined streets. Leaving the river behind, they drove through the busy inner-city precincts, stopping continually at traffic lights. She recognised Brunswick Street and realised they were almost there.

Home for the next four weeks. Warm sunshine, clear blue skies, birdsong, and springtime flowers. In contrast, Aunt Marilyn could expect grey skies, drizzle, chilly mornings and a small balcony.

Hopefully there'd be a late summer so she could enjoy the delights Malvern offered at this time of year.

Her opportunity for a real conversation about the house swap came when she and Aunt Marilyn were settled on the front veranda with a pot of tea and a plate of pumpkin scones.

"It's lovely to be here again," Joanne said. "But I can't imagine why you'd swap this for Malvern, especially now." She gestured towards the river and the parkland in front of the house.

Aunt Marilyn drank her tea in silence before meeting her eyes.

"I knew you'd be curious. And I'm sure it'll sound foolish," she began. "But there's someone I really want to meet up with again. Someone from long ago. Before I met your uncle."

Someone Aunt Marilyn had known more than fifty years ago? Joanne tried to grasp the implications of this.

"And he's living in Malvern?"

Of course it was a man Aunt Marilyn was referring to. Yet she'd never mentioned anyone. Perhaps now she was on her own, she'd allowed herself to reminisce a little?

Aunt Marilyn had become a widow four years ago. She nodded.

"Robert contacted me recently. He's not well enough to fly over. He suggested I stay with him. But…"

"But you'd rather have your own place?" Joanne finished,

Aunt Marilyn patted her hand.

"I knew you'd understand, Jo." She paused. "I haven't told anyone else. My children might not understand and they could feel upset."

"Tell me about Robert."

"Robert and I were engaged," she said. "I was only nineteen. You can imagine how our parents reacted."

Joanne remembered battles with her own parents. What must it have been like in the 1960s?

"What happened?"

"His parents separated us in the only way they knew how. They moved to Malvern."

"And then Uncle Joseph turned up?"

"That was a few years later," she said.

"Did you love him in the same way?"

"We had a wonderful marriage and I've never had any regrets," Aunt Marilyn said. "But I've never forgotten Robert. And he told me that he's never forgotten me."

"Did Robert marry?"

"Yes. And he has two sons. He's been on his own for the last ten years."

"How did he find you again?"

"He joined Facebook to stay in touch with his grandchildren. One day he typed my name into the search bar."

Joanne's mind worked overtime.

So, Aunt Marilyn was on Facebook? And she must've used her maiden name. Why would she do that?

Was she subconsciously hoping that Robert would find her? Who else only knew her by her maiden name?

The following days were a blur of sleep, disorientation and eating at odd hours. Before she knew it, Joanne was at the airport again, waving off her aunt.

I could almost envy Aunt Marilyn, she thought. *Finding true love not once but twice in her lifetime. And having the courage to follow her heart again at the age of seventy-five.*

"And look at me," she whispered to herself. "One failed marriage and nobody interesting on the horizon."

Not the position she'd expected to find herself in with her fortieth birthday approaching.

She tried to shift this thought from her mind as she drove back to New Farm, focusing instead on the spectacular jacarandas. It wasn't safe to daydream.

And why would he develop a relationship with someone who lived on the other side of the world?

He remained by the gates as she drove inside, closing them after her.

She settled into the new routine of feeding chickens at daybreak and taking Forrest for long walks through the park. Managing Aunt Marilyn's garden required at least an hour's work every day – hosing, composting, pruning and trying to keep on top of the subtropical weeds.

In between these new commitments, she had a steady flow of copy-editing work for her regular clients.

An expression of uncertainty crossed his face. "Hasn't Marilyn told you?"

Anthony was weeding his footpath as she drove up. She was surprised and pleased when he walked over to open the heavy wrought-iron gates for her.

She still hadn't seen much sign of life next door and she took a deep breath.

"Things seem very quiet at yours," she said, lowering her window to thank him.

An expression of uncertainty crossed his face. "Hasn't Marilyn told you?"

"Told me what?"

"Shannon left a few years ago now. I have Emily at the weekends."

What could she say?

"I'm sorry. I had no idea."

"Shannon didn't want any more children, but I did. It got so bad that we seemed to fight all the time."

Listening to him, Joanne's emotions were in freefall. *He's free,* was her first overwhelming thought.

But it might not be true. Good-looking, intelligent men of forty were an endangered species. He'd be on the radar of every available woman in the vicinity.

The following Saturday morning as she headed out the gate with Forrest, she noticed a blue sedan pull up next door. A young girl in black leggings and a green striped top leaped out and ran into Anthony's arms. The woman put a sleepover bag by the gate, spoke briefly to him and drove away.

Should she stay and meet Emily?

Maybe another time.

The park had been quiet during the week. Today there were family groups setting up picnics, dogs everywhere, and teenagers zooming along the riverside path on their E-scooters.

Forrest constantly pulled on the lead, excited by all the activity.

After the walk, it was time to restock the pantry. She had no difficulty finding the supermarket in Merthyr Village. As she wheeled her trolley to the checkout, she noticed her favourite digestive biscuits from England and grabbed two packets.

Forrest was at the front gate barking when she drove up. She realised with ➜

a pang that she hadn't thought to buy him any dog treats.

She was unpacking her groceries when there was a knock. Walking into the hall, she recognised the tall silhouette behind the stained-glass panels. What was Anthony doing here?

As she opened the door, a little girl thrust a posy of pansies into her hands.

"I'm Emily. And I'm five." She was missing several front teeth. "Daddy said you'd make us tea if I'm good."

Anthony clapped a hand over his eyes in mock despair.

"Have you forgotten what else Daddy said, sweetie?"

She scrunched up her eyes.

"Sorry, Daddy." And then she grinned up at Joanne endearingly.

"A cup of tea is a great idea, Emily," Joanne said warmly. "Would you like to come and help me make it?"

"She always visits your aunt," Anthony explained. "I hope you don't mind."

"You're both very welcome." Turning back to Emily, she asked with a smile, "What's your favourite tea?"

"Peppermint, please. In the blue cup with the rooster."

Her eyes met Anthony's.

"What would you like?"

"Marilyn usually makes Yorkshire tea."

He seemed very much at home. Joanne couldn't help wondering how often he visited her aunt. And whether he'd continue to drop in…

He will if he feels welcome, said a little voice in her brain, as she put a plate of digestives on the table.

Emily swooped on them, taking one with each hand.

"Oi! You're lucky she's not an octopus," Anthony joked, as they walked out onto the veranda.

Joanne sat on the old cane sofa. Emily immediately sat beside her.

"What are you and Daddy doing today?" Joanne asked.

Emily's answer surprised her.

"Daddy wants to go to Old McDonald's Farm," she said. "Will you come too?"

"Old McDonald's Farm?" she echoed, looking across at Anthony.

"That's what we call Rosewood Produce. It's an animal feed store," he explained. "I promised Marilyn I'd keep you supplied with chicken food, plus kibble for Forrest."

"There's no need –" she began.

"Emily's counting on it," he said, a pleading look in his eyes.

So she agreed.

Emily shrieked with excitement, spilling lukewarm peppermint tea onto her shorts and yelping.

The visit ended abruptly, Emily insisting she needed to change.

"I'll be outside at two o'clock," Anthony said over his shoulder, as she dragged him down the hall.

He was true to his word. Just on two o'clock, the black Toyota pick-up pulled up outside.

Emily chattered all the way.

On the following Friday, Aunt Marilyn phoned. She sounded much younger than her years.

"I can't tell you how good it is to see Robert again," she began.

Joanne heard of long conversations, gentle walks and leisurely cream teas.

"I don't think four weeks will be enough," Marilyn said wistfully, as she ended the call.

Joanne was feeling the same. The camaraderie between her and Anthony was steadily growing and sometimes there was the sense of something deeper.

But it was impossible.

Wasn't it?

Seven years ago, she'd flown back to Malvern after her holiday here. She'd met someone else, but it hadn't lasted.

What would she do this time? With each passing day, she felt more and more reluctant to leave.

By the time the house swap had reached the three-week mark, not a day went by without Joanne seeing Anthony.

Each week he'd suggest she accompany him on a trip somewhere.

"I don't think four weeks will be enough," Marilyn said wistfully

She pointed out her school, the Storey Bridge and the horses grazing in paddocks once they left suburbia.

It was the same at the produce store.

"This is Buddy," she said, leading Joanne to a cage where an Indian Ringneck parakeet stared back at them. "And there's the alpacas."

She dragged Joanne to see the huge pens of chickens, ducks and geese, alongside yards with contented pigs, cows, goats, Shetland ponies – and two shaggy, doe-eyed alpacas.

No wonder Emily loved coming here.

His work as a landscape consultant took him all over the place. Yesterday she'd caught the car ferry to Stradbroke Island with him. His client had recently moved there and knew little about coastal gardening.

Last week, they'd driven up the range to Toowoomba to help a woman on acreage who wanted a cottage garden for the annual Toowoomba Festival of Flowers. Next week he was seeing someone in Tamborine Village, whose garden sloped steeply.

Time was racing by. ➤

Did he feel it too? she wondered.

A knock at the door disturbed her reverie. She was surprised to see Anthony was on his own. It was her last Saturday in New Farm before flying back.

"Where's Emily?" she asked.

"She's caught the flu so she's not visiting this weekend."

Joanne's heart fell. She wouldn't have a chance to say goodbye.

Why did it matter so much?

Anthony was looking at her.

"I don't suppose…" His voice faded.

"We'll never know if you don't ask," she replied. Then she bit her lip, wishing she hadn't spoken.

"I need to go to Rosewood Produce," he said. "But you'll have things to do."

a phone call startled her. It was an apologetic Aunt Marilyn.

"I need to stay a bit longer." She sounded close to tears.

"Has something happened?" Joanne asked, alarmed.

"Robert has to have an operation. He's going to need help while he recovers."

There was a long pause while Joanne considered her options.

Aunt Marilyn continued, "I want to be the one looking after him, you see?"

"Will you be moving into his place?"

"His cottage is a bit small for two. I'm sorry for springing this on you. Could you possibly house-sit for another fortnight?"

It wasn't a hard decision. Her clients were all online. The weather was glorious.

"Maybe we could walk out to the island on the sand bar if it's low tide"

"Actually I'd love to come along."

"Really?" He blinked.

She nodded. "And maybe we could drive on to Wellington Point? Is that fish and chip shop still there?" The one he'd taken her to seven years ago.

"It certainly is."

"Maybe we could walk out to the island on the sand bar if it's low tide."

"It's a date," he said. "Ten o'clock?"

It was the first time either of them had used the word "date". Joanne hoped with all her heart it wouldn't be the last.

That evening she relived every moment of the day, flicking through the photos on her phone.

There was one taken by a teenager who was fishing from the sand bar. Anthony's arm was across her shoulders, her head nestled into his chest. They looked for all the world like a couple.

She was looking at the photo when

It felt as though she was being gifted with an endless summer. A chance to reconnect with her heart and think about what she really wanted in life.

If she didn't stay, she knew for certain that she'd regret it for the rest of her life.

"Yes, I can stay another fortnight," she said. Yet as she spoke, she realised how much harder it would be to leave in two weeks' time.

After the call ended, Joanne picked up a bottle of Merlot and walked round to next door. Her heart fluttered as she rang Anthony's doorbell and heard him walking down the hall.

"I'm here for another two weeks," she said. "Shall we celebrate?"

Reaching up, she kissed him on the lips, then explained Marilyn's circumstances. His eyes brimmed with emotion as he drew her inside.

"Would it be wrong to wish Robert a very long convalescence?" Ⓜ

Brain Boosters

Sudoku

	3			7				6
			4	1	7	5		
5				8			9	2
7					2			
	8						3	
		5						8
1	2		8					7
	4	8	2	6				
6				9			2	

Fill in each of the blank squares with the numbers 1 to 9, so that each row, each column and each 3x3 cell contains all the numbers from 1 to 9.

Turn To Page 173 For Solutions

Word Wheel

You have ten minutes to find as many words as possible using the letters in the wheel. Each word must be three letters or more and contain the central letter. Use each letter once and no plurals, foreign words or porper nouns are allowed. There is at least one nine-letter word.

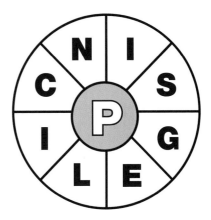

Heart And Soul

Her Elvis-mad husband might be a bit much, but
that's why she loves him . . . isn't it?

By Christine Sutton

Anne sipped her bright orange mocktail, wondering what her new friend Reece was making of Barry's performance. Up on the hotel's tiny stage, the portly, grey-haired man continued to warble his way through *Suspicious Minds*, or sus-pish-uss mi-yinds, as Barry would have it. Reece leaned in closer.

"Your husband certainly throws himself into it," she said warmly.

"Heart and soul," Anne agreed, using another Elvis title. Barry was cranking up the volume ready for his big finale, causing two more hotel guests to scurry towards the exit.

"And not just karaoke," Reece went on. "Chatting to him at dinner, I got the impression he loves life in general."

rheumaticky right knee, his leg gave way and he disappeared from view.

Reece put down her drink.

"Oh, dear," she said, rising. "I think he may have just fallen off his high-heeled sneakers."

Anne smothered a giggle. "Don't be cruel," she quipped, joining in the fun. Reece looked at her apologetically.

"Actually, Anne, he does seem to have fallen off the stage."

Leaping to her feet, Anne hurried to where Barry lay gazing at the sluggishly revolving ceiling fan.

"Hello, love," he croaked. "Uh, like the King said, 'I'm all shook up'."

And he did it while impersonating Elvis, you say?" The young doctor squinted at Barry's X-ray.

"Hello, love. Uh, like the King said, 'I'm all shook up'"

"Yes, Barry's an enthusiast about pretty much everything," Anne agreed, praying silently that he'd at least give the pelvic thrust a miss.

"Hmmm… And we can't BUILD a dre-ye-yeam…"

It was on the tail-end of "yeam" that it happened. As he swung the mic stand sideways and tried an unwise lunge on his

"Yes," Anne confirmed, "and on the first day of our tour, too."

The man couldn't contain his surprise.

"You mean he tours as Elvis?"

"Oh, no," she amended. "We're touring Derbyshire and the Peak District. Last year it was Graceland. This year was my choice, but when we got to the hotel we found it was karaoke night. ➔

"Barry can't resist karaoke, you see."

The doctor pressed his lips together.

"Well, Mr Presley – sorry, Priestly – if it's any consolation, at least the injury's appropriate. You've damaged your pelvis. You're going to need a hip op."

Anne could have sworn she saw a flicker of relief on Barry's face. Could the prospect of surgery really be more appealing than sightseeing with her?

He lifted his shoulders in a helpless shrug. "Sorry, love. Looks like you'll have to carry on without me. You go ahead and do the tours, though. Be a shame for us both to miss out."

She was about to decline when she paused. Every holiday since Barry's retirement had been Elvis-related.

better than sitting in the hospital visitors' room waiting for Barry to wake up."

"Yes, and then when he did come round, to be told off for wasting the tickets," Anne added.

Hearing chuckles from the women around her, she felt a glow of female solidarity. Normally the attention was all on Barry, so it was quite a novelty being heard. Gathering up their belongings, they got off the coach.

Strolling beside the tree-fringed lake, Reece told Anne about her new job as wardrobe mistress in her local theatre.

It was an animated account full of amusing anecdotes, yet Anne's thoughts started to drift.

Could the prospect of surgery be more appealing than sightseeing with her?

From his birthplace in Tupelo, to noisy Las Vegas, scene of his sell-out stage shows, to last year's visit to Graceland, his home and final resting place, all were interesting enough, but she yearned for something that didn't focus solely on Barry's idol. Well, this was it – and she was going to make the most of it.

"OK, Barry, love. If you're sure."

As the coach pulled into the car park for their second stop of the morning, Anne put her phone back in her bag.

"The ward sister says he's recovering well and I'm to stop worrying and get on with enjoying my day."

"Quite right, too," Reece said stoutly. "I don't think you heard a word the guide said about Florence Nightingale's home."

"I didn't," Anne admitted. "I was so looking forward to seeing it, too."

"Well, you've done absolutely the right thing coming today," Reece said. "Much

Would Barry's accident knock the stuffing out of him? she wondered.

"He'll be back on his feet in no time, you'll see," Reece said, when Anne apologised. "Why not take a few photos, show him what he's missing?"

"Photos," Anne exclaimed. "Good idea." She dug out Barry's camera from her pocket and fired off a few shots, adding, "Not that I think he feels he's missing much."

"Sightseeing not his thing?"

"Not this sort of sightseeing," Anne said. "As you probably gathered, Barry's idea of a great holiday is anything to do with Elvis. Throw in fruit machines and showgirl razzmatazz and he's in seventh heaven. We're chalk and cheese in many respects, yet somehow we work."

She followed Reece up a flight of steps to a grassy incline laid out with twenty or so wooden picnic tables. Nearby was a café and a souvenir shop.

"So, you alternate? One year Vegas, the next Venice or something?" Reece guessed, as they unpacked their lunches.

"I wish! Barry gets bored trailing around museums and galleries, so there's little point in suggesting them. I chose this time because it's my sixtieth next week."

"Oh, happy birthday for then," Reece broke in. "And has it always been that way? Barry making the decisions?"

"Pretty much," Anne said. "I've never been a very assertive person. Barry says that when I was on God's workbench He must've had hiccups, because although my sweetness dial is on ten – his assessment, not mine – my self-confidence is hovering just above zero.

"And I say, in that case, when Barry was being worked on, God must've sneezed and set everything to max!"

"Well, you're here today and I for one am liking this new, independent you," Reece declared, biting into an egg roll.

"I must confess, she's growing on me too!" Anne laughed, doing the same with her BLT. "So, what about you, Reece? What brings you here alone?"

"I needed some time away from my husband. We've been bickering a lot. I wanted a chance to think things through."

"And ended up saddled with us old codgers," Anne smiled. "Poor you."

"Not at all," Reece said. "Barry's great fun and you're lovely. I just wonder – and I hope you won't mind me saying this, Anne – if that larger-than-life personality of his doesn't smother yours, just a bit?"

Anne waggled her head, as though weighing it up. "I've always been quiet. I'm the youngest of five girls, rarely got a word in edgeways growing up. If anything, Barry brought me out of myself. Together we've done things I would never have dared do on my own."

"So how did you two meet?"

"I was working in a tearoom on the

coast, a bashful thirty-six-year-old with no expectations of ever getting married," Anne said, pushing the straw into a carton of apple juice. "Then, one rainy afternoon, in came this human dynamo named Barry. He'd just come from a job interview at the local radio station.

"With his gift of the gab and love of music, broadcasting was perfect for him. We got chatting and something clicked." Her eyes sparkled, as if she still couldn't believe her luck.

"You said earlier that you'd been bickering with your husband, Reece. Do you mind me asking what about?"

The younger woman sighed. "Working in the theatre means I do funny hours. It can be hard on family life. Now David wants me to give it all up to have a baby."

"And you don't want one?" Anne asked gently.

"One day, yes, but I'm only thirty-three." Reece gestured with what remained of her roll. "Lots of women leave having babies until their late thirties, or even older. What about you, ➤

Anne – do you have any children?"

"We wanted them," she said quietly, "but it didn't happen."

Reece frowned in dismay.

"Oh, I'm sorry, Anne. I didn't mean to sound flippant."

Anne patted her hand.

"Don't apologise. We came to terms with it a long time ago. You find ways to fill the void." She swivelled round and dropped the sandwich wrappings in the bin behind her. "Anyway, we've just got time to visit the gift shop. I'd like to get something fun for Barry."

Twenty minutes later, they headed back to the coach.

"Your husband's going to love those speciality beers," Anne said, as they resumed their seats.

"And I can so see Barry in that muscle man pinny," Reece laughed. "*I'm a man in Peak condition.* Perfect." She lowered her voice. "What you were saying earlier, Anne, about not being able to have children. Was there anything you could've done differently?"

"Regrettably, no. Barry and I simply met too late. You were right about some women leaving it longer nowadays, and everyone's got to do what's right for them, but it's not always plain sailing.

"If you have a choice, Reece, don't wait too long, hmm?"

Her companion nodded.

"Thank you, Anne. Wish Barry a speedy recovery for me. I think I'll head home tomorrow. David and I have some talking to do."

Anne smiled.

"I'm glad. Be happy, both of you."

Walking through the ward that evening, Anne was surprised to see that half the beds were empty, their occupants nowhere to be seen. Hearing a burst of laughter, she moved quietly towards a four-bedded side room.

In the first bay was Barry, his leg supported in a pulley. In the next one along a tattooed youth looked to have suffered a similar injury, for their plastered limbs made a matching pair. Ranged around them, helpless with mirth as Barry regaled them with a colourful account of his mishap, were the absentee patients.

"Classic, man," spluttered the tattooed teen, wiping tears from his eyes. "Elvis breaks pelvis falling off stage."

"You couldn't make it up!" managed another, trying to catch his breath.

Watching them laughing and joshing together despite their assorted ills, Anne felt a rush of affection for her big-hearted spouse. Loud and brash he may be, but for these men he was as good a tonic as any medication.

Setting her features in a mock-stern expression, she stepped into the room.

"Barry Priestly, is that you causing all that rumpus?"

He shrank back against the pillows.

"Oops, caught in the act, boys. Quick, skedaddle while you can."

With back slaps and handshakes, his chuckling audience melted away. Anne took their place beside his bed.

"Hello, love, how are you?"

"Good," he answered. "How was your day? I missed you."

"Lovely. We'll definitely have to come back again." She smiled fondly and took his hand. "In the words of a certain Mr Presley, Barry, have I told you lately that I love you?"

His expression softened.

"I love you too, more than I can say. So, um, how about a little less conversation and...?" He pointed to his lips.

Laughing, affectionately, Anne leaned in and kissed her exasperating, exuberant, wonderful spouse. Ⓜ

Brain Boosters

Codeword

Each letter of the alphabet has been replaced by a number. The numbers for the first name of our pictured celebrity are given. Work out which number represents which letter in the grid to reveal which children's TV show Matt Baker once presented.

21	26	20	6	19	7	24	25	19	7	14		24	7	12
16		21		22		23		21		6		23		25
16	23	11	11	18		2	19	24	7	2	2	16	23	20
25		7		13		10			8		16		6
20	23	15	1	7	14		9	7	17	7	20	20	7	14
		1							20		7		25
6	15	7	24	19						7	14	6	19
13													7
13	25	19	19							2	19	25	15	14
21		23		15							4		
14	21	1	1	7	24	7	20		21	26	19	23	2	7
7		26		7			3		24		25		15
2	17	21	24	14	16	6	2	22		25	3	19	7	14
19		25		20		13		25		10		6		7
18	7	19		7	5	8	7	24	6	7	15	3	7	14

A B C D E F G H I J K L M N O P Q R S T U V W X Y Z

1	2	3	4	5	6	7	8	9	10	11	12	13
												M
14	15	16	17	18	19	20	21	22	23	24	25	26
					T						**A**	

26	20	23	7		8	7	19	7	24
							T		

Turn To
Page 173 For
Solutions

Bedding In

Maggie was proud of her bright daughter – but letting go was the hardest thing...

By Marie Penman

PICTURE: SHUTTERSTOCK

The summer, they all agreed, had been perfect – a lovely family holiday in a villa in France, a few day trips to the coast and an amazing party in the back garden for Lucy's eighteenth birthday.

But throughout all of that, and despite the laughter and smiling faces, Maggie had felt a niggling dread at the back of her mind, knowing that the summer would end and the day she didn't want to think about would arrive.

Lucy, her only child, was leaving to go away to university.

"I'll only be fifty miles away, Mum!"

Lucy kept telling her. "It's not like I'm going to the other side of the world."

Maggie knew she was being silly, and fully supported her daughter's move into adulthood, but even so, the very thought of her leaving, of her bedroom lying empty, brought tears to Maggie's eyes.

As the temperatures dropped and the leaves began to change colour, the final days of summer drifted into autumn, and mother and daughter worked together to get ready for the Big Day.

"I'm thinking of a jungle print for my new bedding, Mum," Lucy remarked one day as they browsed the aisles of their local homeware store. "It sends out a message to my flatmates and new friends that I'm bold and uncompromising."

Maggie smiled as she picked up cushions and blankets, and stroked them to see how soft they felt. She loved the fact that her little girl was so confident and optimistic as she headed into this next chapter of her life, and wished she could feel the same.

Once Lucy left, it would just be Maggie and her husband, Jim, at home. What on earth would they do with themselves?

Finally, the day arrived and the three of them loaded up the car ➔

together, filling every nook and cranny.

"Don't they have shops where you're going, love?" Jim remarked as he squashed in a giant box of cereal, a bunch of bananas and several packets of biscuits.

Lucy tutted.

"It's just to get me started, Dad – I don't want to be doing my shopping when there could be parties to go to!"

The drive took them just over an hour, then almost the same again to find a vacant parking spot. Between them, they carried the bags, boxes and cases up the flights of stairs, and then stared at the tiny bedroom – more like a cupboard – and wondered where everything was going to fit.

Maggie felt her daughter's absence so strongly, she could almost grasp it. As her gaze took in the discarded hairbands, empty sweet wrappers and odd socks lying around – Lucy could never be described as tidy – she sighed and sat down on the edge of the bed.

She remembered all the chats they'd shared, the discussions about schoolwork and friends and boy bands, and wondered who she could talk to now…

Maggie flopped back on the bed, feeling despondent. She could hear Jim pottering about downstairs, putting the kettle on and loading up the washing machine, and thought about joining him. Maybe just a few more minutes lying

Maggie felt her daughter's absence so strongly, she could almost grasp it

Lucy giggled and said she'd manage somehow, then told her parents that she was fine and that they were free to go.

Desperate to prolong the moment, Maggie offered to make up the bed (that lovely new duvet cover!) but Jim said Lucy wasn't a baby and she obviously wasn't stupid, seeing as she was starting university, so they could probably leave her to it.

They laughed and hugged and said goodbye, and Lucy promised to come back to visit soon. Then Maggie and Jim drove home mainly in silence, thinking about how their little family was now even smaller.

Was it Maggie's imagination or did the house definitely feel emptier when they walked in?

She went upstairs to change into her comfy clothes and couldn't resist peeping into Lucy's bedroom.

Looking around, smelling the familiar scent of perfume, hairspray and fake tan,

on Lucy's bed, hugging her pillow and breathing in her smell…

She felt tears sliding down her cheeks as she lay still, but she couldn't get comfy.

There was a bump in the bed.

She pulled back the duvet and spotted a gift bag hidden under the covers.

There was a card inside it, alongside a half-empty bottle of Lucy's perfume.

"Mum, I hope you aren't lying on my bed, crying because you miss me!! I just want to thank you for being the best mum ever – without you I couldn't have done this. Spray this perfume around to remind you of me, lol. See you in a couple of weeks!!"

And Maggie laughed and cried, and understood that she hadn't lost her little girl. She'd just done what any parent should do, and allowed her child to grow, to thrive and to blossom into a happy young adult.

She got up, made the bed and headed downstairs for a cup of tea with Jim. ⓜ

Brain Boosters

Kriss Kross

Try to fit all of the listed words back into the grid.

4 letters	ORDER	8 letters	10 letters
LASH	**6 letters**	EXERTION	STEREOTYPE
MYTH	CRANNY	MISOGYNY	TRANSCRIPT
SCOW	RENOWN	**9 letters**	**11 letters**
TYRE	**7 letters**	NEWSAGENT	PRODIGALITY
5 letters	RETHINK	TROOPSHIP	TOPOGRAPHIC
GRIND	TATTLER		

Turn To Page 173 For Solutions

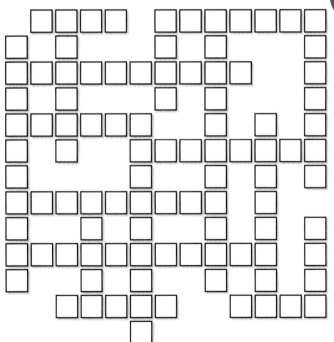

Hallowe'en Magic

When it came to love, only one name was truly carved on his heart...

By Carrie Hewlett

Mike still felt uncertain when he and Donna arrived at the tattoo studio. Not because he was scared of getting one. He actually had several, including a majestic phoenix on his back.

No, it was because of what Donna wanted him to get.

She'd nuzzled against his chest a few weeks prior. "Let's get matching heart tattoos. I love Mike and I love Donna. I can book us an appointment at my tattoo parlour. Edwardo is brilliant.

"Though if we're having them done at the same time, we'll have to make sure someone else good can do yours."

She'd gazed at him suggestively, running her finger down his arm.

And on the spur of the moment, and being totally smitten, he'd agreed.

You're with Edwardo, like usual," the girl on reception told Donna, before glancing at Mike. "You're booked in with Willow, one of our guest tattooists. I think you'll be pleased. She's magical."

"Thanks." For some reason a faint fluttering of anxiety still tinged his stomach. He and Donna had only been together for six months. Was he doing ➔

the right thing? Firmly, he pushed the doubts away.

She was a great girl; fun to be with, and totally gorgeous. Of course he loved her.

They didn't have to wait long and after Donna had been whisked away, Mike was directed along a winding corridor, before being led into a large room with autumnal sunlight spilling in through creamy blinds.

Mike tried to ignore the tendrils of doubt still swirling inside.

"It's what we both want."

"Something plain and simple or are you happy for me to freestyle, like this?"

While they'd been talking, she'd drawn up a design on the computer.

Mike gave the drawing a cursory glance. It was excellent. "I like that."

She was a great girl; fun to be with and totally gorgeous. Of course he loved her

A woman sat to one side, a curtain of blonde hair, the ends tipped with blue and green, hiding her face until she looked up; his breath caught as his gaze met eyes of deepest forest green.

"Hi, I'm Willow."

"Mike."

She smiled and he felt his pulse quicken. She was beautiful. His gaze fell on her left hand. No ring. Good. But then he admonished himself for even thinking along those lines when he was about to have a tattoo of a heart with Donna's name. How could he do that to her?

All he knew was that he was attracted to Willow. Was this a sign that he shouldn't get it done?

"Take a seat and tell me what you'd like." She continued to smile and again he felt his heart race.

Taking a deep breath, he tried to focus his mind as he smiled back at her.

"My girlfriend wants me to get a heart with her name engraved at its centre."

"And is that what you want?"

"What?"

"You said it's what she wants. But is it what you want?" Willow continued to gaze at him with an open and warm expression. "Only in my experience, people often ask for one thing when in reality they want something else."

"In which case, take a seat. What colour did you have in mind?"

"Red, I guess."

"OK…"

"No. Wait."

His gaze had rested momentarily upon a painting on the far wall and the colours transfixed him. Almost pearlescent and reminding him of the ocean.

"Any chance of similar colours to that?" He pointed.

She followed his gaze, and her eyes crinkled at the corners. "No worries."

They chattered generally as Willow worked and Mike barely felt a thing.

"You're good," he said admiringly.

"Thanks. Expressing your art is one of the kindest things you can do for yourself as you can let your creativity convey your inner emotions."

"But aren't you doing what other people want?"

She gave an enigmatic smile and he felt a longing deep within his soul.

"I always add a touch of me. Nothing too showy, as I want to please the client, but something that sparks my imagination and I can weave into the design."

"I wouldn't have thought you'd be able to do much with a heart with a name inside."

"Oh, you'd be surprised. There.

I've finished. Would you like to see?"

"Thanks."

She held up a mirror so that he could see the top of his arm and he felt an odd sensation running through his body. Not just appreciation and admiration, but something else. Something electric, like just before a storm when the air thickens.

His breath quickened as an image flashed into his mind like a beam of light which he brushed away quickly.

An image of him with Willow. Which, considering he was with Donna, was not going to happen. Ever.

Walking back to the car, Donna linked arms. "I'm pleased with Edwardo's tattoo, but yours seems a bit fancy."

"I like it because it's different." When Willow had shown him, he'd felt a lump in his throat at its intricacy. The heart was almost mystical in design. It didn't quite meet in the middle, and it almost seemed to flow, like the waves, at the edges. Greens, blues, opalescent pinks, all merged as if from one centre point.

As if Willow were trying to bring the magic and the love of the sea all together in one place.

And there seemed to be a secret contained within the heart. The "O" of Donna was almost like seaweed entwining its way through the heart. Or was it more like willow leaves…? Mike shook himself.

It was so much better than he'd ever hoped. When he'd commented on its beauty, Willow had given him a radiant look, her eyes shining like soft stars.

And if Mike hadn't known better, he'd have said that he'd felt as though magic was in the air. "If you're not happy, then come back and see me."

"No. I love it. It's perfect. Thank you."

"Good. But I will see you again soon, Mike. I'm certain."

His heart had leapt at her comment.

What did she mean? But he'd just smiled in response, not knowing what else to say.

He didn't realise then how true her remark was. Or how she'd known that they'd meet again. It was several months later, and Hallowe'en was fast approaching. He and Donna had parted ways not long after the tattoo.

They'd started snapping at each other, especially when he didn't do as Donna asked. And he knew deep within that he didn't want to be with her. She seemed to feel the same way, flouncing off after an argument telling him that he wasn't the man she thought he was.

Not long after that, he'd seen her on her tattooist Edwardo's arms, which should have been no big surprise as, on asking around, it seemed that she'd been seeing Edwardo behind his back ever since they'd had the matching tattoos done.

Due to work commitments, he'd not got round to booking an appointment to get his tattoo inked over, but it was something he was keen to get sorted as soon as he could.

One morning while he was shaving, an image of Willow came to mind. And with it, a sudden yearning to be with her.

Crazy, he told himself, wondering if she was back at the tattoo parlour.

OK, he might run into Donna or Edwardo, but he didn't care.

"Sorry. She's not been back for ages. I think she's busy with other stuff," was the response when he rang.

"I don't suppose I could get a contact number for her?"

He had a feeling what the answer would be, but it was worth trying.

"Sorry. We don't give out personal information."

"Could you take a note of my contact details and if she returns let me know?"➤

"Sure," the girl said. "I don't see why not."

"And have you any slots available next week with anyone? Only I'd like a tattoo inked over."

"We're fairly busy, but I could slot you in in a few weeks' time. The seventeenth at 6pm?"

"Thanks. That's brilliant."

At least he now had an appointment, which was good.

He turned his mind to the Hallowe'en party his friend had asked him along to that weekend, which sounded fun.

Wearing a flowing cloak from a party a few years earlier over a shirt and black trousers, he affixed some Dracula teeth

"I guessed." She laughed, and her eyes lit up in playful fun before she cast her gaze enquiringly round the room.

"No Donna?"

"You remember her name?"

Mike was surprised. After all, it was several months ago, and surely she must see loads of people.

"I remember some." She gazed up at him with an expression of utmost honesty and he felt his heart jerk.

"We're no longer together. Split up not long after the tattoo, to be honest."

He shrugged. "I'm not sure why we stayed together as long as we did."

"Maybe because you had hope. We all believe we'll meet the person of our

"It's as though they pull at our heart strings and we can no longer stay apart"

he'd bought online. Along with some fake blood, he felt suitably dressed up.

The party was in full swing when he arrived and he wound his way through partygoers to the kitchen where he grabbed a beer.

"Hello again."

A warm voice nudged his awareness. Turning, his heart leapt at seeing Willow wearing a fetching off-the-shoulder black lace number, long lace gloves and high heels. Her blonde hair this time was tipped with midnight blue, bubble-gum pink and forest greens. On anyone else it might have looked ridiculous, but on her it seemed to accentuate her very loveliness and unique personality.

She wore a black fascinator in her hair with a diamante brooch at its centre.

"You look amazing," he breathed.

She smiled, the same warm smile he remembered. "Thanks. I'm a witch."

He waved a hand over his costume. "Dracula."

dreams, and we keep trying till we do. And sometimes we mistake love for something else.

"But when we do meet that special person we're supposed to spend the rest of our life with we know, deep within."

She lay a hand across her chest, her expression heartfelt. "It's as though they pull at our heart strings and we can no longer stay apart, two magnets drawn inextricably to each other."

Mike gazed at her, feeling a pull to be closer to her.

But was she with someone? He didn't think he could bear it if she was.

As though she read his mind, she shrugged one elegant shoulder, drawing his gaze to her lightly tanned skin.

"To answer your question, I came with friends, but…"

She laughed, a slight tinkly sound that had his insides seesawing with emotion.

"They seem to have vanished. Maybe they're enjoying the party too much."

"How did you…?"

She laughed again. A delicious sound to his ears. "I'm a witch."

He grinned. "You must be. Would you like to dance?"

It seemed as though the rest of the partygoers faded into the background as he held her in his arms. He could smell faint tinges of apple blossom wafting from her hair as they moved in perfect time to the music. It felt to Mike as though they were the only two people in the room.

Was this what true love was? For he could think of no other reason for the way he was feeling. Her scent, her body, her smile, her almond-shaped eyes that every now and then gazed up at him with a twinkle as if they contained stardust.

It seemed natural several hours later for him to take her home.

And when she turned to kiss him goodnight, it felt as though Cupid himself had drawn and fired his bow.

"When can I see you again?"

"Tomorrow."

The next few days they spent every minute they could together. Meeting after work, romantic walks in the autumnal air, wrapped up warmly in thick jackets, gloves and scarves or just cuddled up on the sofa. ➜

"Why do you only do guest spots with tattoo parlours?" he asked one evening when they were snuggled up in front of his fire. Its radiant flame seemed to illuminate her golden hair, which was now tipped with russet reds and earthy browns.

"Because I like to choose my clients." Puzzled, his brow furrowed.

"But surely you don't know the people the studio might be booking for you."

"But I do." She unconsciously twirled one finger through her tresses before her mouth curved into a small smile. "Didn't I tell you at the party that I was a witch?"

His brow furrowed further. "Yes… and I was Dracula. But it was a Hallowe'en party. We were all dressed up."

could see his upper arm in the living room mirror. His eyes widened in shock and disbelief. "But… how? Did you do it when I was asleep one night?"

"No. It happened all on its own since we've been together. That's when I knew for sure that you were the man for me.

"The spell I did was a truth spell. One where I asked for the name of your true love to be emblazoned on your arm within the heart I was inking.

"I wasn't even sure myself as I had such strong feelings for you. I knew I had to be careful not to allow my emotions to overwhelm the design.

"I felt sure you and Donna weren't meant to be together. But though I sensed

"Although I don't always use magic I have to admit casting a small spell"

"Yes…" she said slowly. "But in my case, it's true. I'm both a tattoo artist and a witch. I only use my powers for good, however, and for picking the right clients. When you rang and booked the appointment, I knew without a shadow of a doubt that we were meant to be together. The timbre of your voice sent through a powerful message to my soul.

"I was aware you were with someone, and please believe me when I tell you I did nothing to break you and Donna up. That happened quite naturally.

"But I knew I wanted to see you again, and although I don't always use magic I have to admit to casting a small spell when I did your tattoo."

Mike half shook his head in bewilderment. "What sort of spell?"

Willow tilted her head to one side and her eyes sparkled. "Why don't you take another look at it?"

Humouring her, Mike rose, pulled off his jumper and angled his body so he

it, I wasn't completely sure whether it was just a physical attraction on my part or something more. We witches aren't infallible, you know.

"I wove a time spell at the same time, one that would gradually reveal the name of the person you were supposed to be with if your heart and mind were in agreement."

Mike gazed again at the tattoo Willow had inked several months prior. One he didn't even bother looking at these days, convinced as he was that he would just see Donna's name.

Only it wasn't Donna's name he was now seeing.

Within the pearlescent heart, another name had appeared. One that he knew he would never want to be inked over.

Willow.

And whether that was magic and she was indeed a witch, or whether Fate had taken a hand in things, all Mike knew was that his love for her would never fade. Ⓜ

Brain Boosters

Sudoku

			2		3			
		4	5				6	2
	9						1	
	1				8	4		
7							2	6
			1			5		3
6			9		4			7
	8	1		5				
	7			3	2	6		

Fill in each of the blank squares with the numbers 1 to 9, so that each row, each column and each 3x3 cell contains all the numbers from 1 to 9.

Turn To Page 173 For Solutions

Word Wheel

You have ten minutes to find as many words as possible using the letters in the wheel. Each word must be three letters or more and contain the central letter. Use each letter once and no plurals, foreign words or porper nouns are allowed. There is at least one nine-letter word.

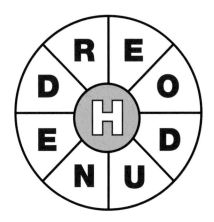

Kismet At Rainbow's End

It seemed too good to be true, how this production brought my past and future together…

By Carol Probyn

Ooh, I'm so excited for you, Sophie! You'll love being a Munchkin!"

We were gazing at the colourful poster advertising *The Wizard of Oz*. Drayton Operatic Dramatic Society were putting on our favourite musical instead of the traditional pantomime this year.

It was a cartoon-like poster, with a Judy Garland-esque Dorothy, flanked by Scarecrow, Tin Man and Lion, skipping

along a spiralling yellow brick road, set in a stylised, Technicolor Munchkinland.

"Whatever," shrugged my nine-year-old granddaughter, pretending indifference, as she strolled off to the children`s rehearsal. But I knew she was thrilled to bits.

I wandered off to the coffee shop with a magazine to wait until she finished. Lucy – my daughter and Sophie`s mum – was in the adult cast, and had taken the chance of some free time to go shopping.

I sipped my coffee, but the magazine remained untouched. I couldn't help thinking how funny it was that life had a habit of repeating itself. For I had been in a similar production thirty years ago.

It was 1992 when I'd been a member of Drayton Operatic Dramatic Society, and we had just started rehearsals for *The Wizard of Oz*.

It had been my second show, the first being *South Pacific*, when I'd sung in the chorus. Robert Martin had played the handsome lieutenant, and it had been love at first sight. By the time rehearsals for *The Wizard of Oz* got started, we were engaged, even though my father insisted I was too young. Heady days.

Robert had been so versatile – from handsome lieutenant to The Scarecrow. His comical antics had stolen the show, so I was told.

"Like to help with these?" Sally,   ➛

one of the theatre volunteers, was pinning miniature rainbows and stars along the wall – replacing the Christmas decorations. I was glad of the distraction.

It had been a good Christmas for our little family, and it had never lost its magic for me, in spite of us all missing my dear Derek whom we had lost five years previously. He would have loved to see his granddaughter blossoming into the happy, confident Munchkin she is today.

Soon the sound of distant, excited voices alerted us to the fact that rehearsals were over. I pinned up the last rainbow and made my way to the foyer.

Sophie bounded towards me.

"I`m going to be a lollipop girl! I sing a line on my own!"

"Enchanting!" Robert grinned.

"Sophie's my granddaughter. She's going to be a lollipop girl, aren't you, darling?" I smoothed her silky blonde hair, feeling the blood rush to my face.

"You, a grandmother? It`s not possible. You look wonderful, Amy. I did hear about Derek. I'm sorry, it can't have been easy for you."

That surprised me, but of course we knew the same people years ago. I hadn't cried for ages, but now, for some absurd reason, I suddenly felt tearful.

There was an embarrassing pause, parents and children milled around us, and even Sophie had stopped fidgeting.

"This really is an incredible coincidence," Robert said.

As we looked into each other's eyes the world stopped turning for an instant

"Brilliant, darling!" I bent to hug her.

"Amy? Amy Lovell?"

The voice was familiar. Towering above me, I would have known him anywhere. For what seemed an age, I was frozen with disbelief. I had been thinking of him shortly before, and here he was.

I looked around for Glinda the good fairy, totally at a loss. Eventually I managed to speak.

"Robert," I croaked, straightening up and clutching my granddaughter. His charismatic good looks were still evident, although he had crinkled nicely round the edges. Grey hair suited him, and I pushed my fingers through my own hair, acutely aware it needed colouring.

"I'd have known you anywhere! You've hardly changed at all!"

Same smile, same charming man.

"What a lovely child." He smiled at my granddaughter. "And what's your name?"

"Sophie Taylor," she trilled.

"I heard you'd moved back. Always hoped I'd bump into you, Drayton being such a small town. And here you are."

"Yes. I came back to be near my daughter and Sophie. Lucy's husband works for the university, so I've come full circle, really."

I concentrated on straightening Sophie's hairband. Full circle! What a stupid thing to say!

"Kismet," he said quietly, and as we looked into each other's eyes the world stopped turning again for an instant.

Kismet would have been DODS' next production after *The Wizard* if I had stayed, if I hadn't moved to Southampton. Kismet, of course, also means "fate".

"I really must be going, Robert. It's been nice seeing you again," I muttered.

Nice! My stomach was in knots, and I wondered if my legs would still work.

"Listen, why don't we meet up for a coffee – or something – sometime?"

I still felt like a rabbit frozen in the headlights, and we were surrounded by other jostling parents and children. A little chorus of *Follow the Yellow Brick Road* had begun in the corner.

Robert was still looking at me, waiting for me to say something.

At that, Lucy my daughter appeared at my elbow. She took Sophie's hand, but not before appraising Robert.

"Hello! Had a lovely time, darling?"

As Sophie began to tell her mother about rehearsals, a young boy about ten ran up to Robert.

"Daddy, Daddy! I'm going to be a lollipop boy!"

"That's great!" Robert laughed. He turned to me. "Didn't you say that Sophie was going to –"

"Your son?"

Before Robert could reply, an attractive young woman materialised beside them, smiled fondly at Robert then bent down to the boy.

"Have a good time, James?"

"Brilliant!" laughed James, hugging his father's knees. Robert glanced at me and I couldn't read the expression on his face. Before I could think, I was hustled towards the exit with my daughter, grandchild and the departing throng.

W ho WAS that attractive man you were talking to, Mum?" Lucy asked me in the car on the way home.

"Oh, just someone I knew years ago. Imagine, he has a son not much older than my granddaughter!" I had found my voice now, alright.

"That's men for you. Mars and Venus and all that!"

"Yes and his wife looks to be about your age! And he had the nerve to invite me for a coffee!"

"Oh, dear. Still, quite flattering though?"

Had I been flattered? Here I was a grandmother, and quite astonished that I could have experienced the rollercoaster of emotions on seeing Robert again. Mars and Venus, Kismet – it was all tosh!

All the same, I couldn't help remembering what had happened a lifetime ago.

I had been eighteen and Robert twenty.

"Promise me you'll always be my leading lady," he had said after the opening night of *South Pacific*. It truly was an enchanted evening, for he had given me a sapphire engagement ring by the end of the production.

I know, it all sounds slushy and clichéd, but that's just how it was. It really did seem like some kind of old-fashioned fairytale.

But fate, or Kismet, had other ideas. My father was transferred to Southampton with his job, and my parents insisted I go with them. I was far too young to get married, they said.

It had been an awful time, lots of arguments and tears, with Robert begging me to stay. In the end, my father said to give it a year to see if our love would stand the test of time. ➜

So I left Drayton, *The Wizard of Oz* and Robert. Robert came to see me for a weekend a few months later, but somehow the magic had faded.

He wrote a kind and gentle letter breaking off our engagement a month after that. The following year, he married Celia Berry, Dorothy's understudy.

And soon afterwards, I was engaged again myself – to Derek.

The following week, I was hovering behind the other parents waiting to pick up Sophie again at the theatre. Silver stars and rainbows were everywhere now.

Robert came up to me.

"Takes you back, eh?"

"Yes." I feigned indifference, but I had applied a little make-up and had my roots done. I had my pride, after all.

All my silly assumptions, and he had experienced a terrible tragedy.

Before I could say anything, the children came bouncing into the foyer.

"Nana, Nana! Everyone clapped James and me when we did our song today!"

I hugged Sophie tight – finding comfort in her vitality, and relieved to dispel my feeling of embarrassment.

James walked up to his father shyly and took his hand.

"Do you think they've cast the Scarecrow? I could do it. 'If I only had a brain, Miss Dorothy'," Robert said, adopting the Scarecrow's voice. He had sensed my discomfort and was diffusing the tension, making us all laugh.

Eventually the others drifted away.

"Now, how about that coffee?" Robert beamed.

The four of us did that little skippy dance along the corridor to the coffee shop

"Too bad you had to rush off last week. We didn't get to arrange that coffee date."

The nerve of the man!

"I'm sorry Robert, but I don't think it's a good idea." I tried to edge away.

"That's a pity," he persisted. "I was totally bowled over seeing you again. My daughter said that she hadn't seen me look so happy in years."

"Your daughter?"

"Yes, Stella. She was here with James last week, you remember? Twenty years between them. James was a late baby, but the joy of our lives. Sadly, though, it was for a very short while. Celia passed away – certain complications…"

I gasped. "I'm so sorry."

"Yes, it was tragic. Stella helps all she can, but I took early retirement as soon as I could. A single parent – who'd have guessed that would happen?"

I make no apologies for finishing my story with a few more clichés from the musicals. After all, that's where the corn is as high as an elephant's eye.

I never got to wash that man right out of my hair, because it felt great when we linked arms and the four of us did that little skippy dance along the corridor to the coffee shop. And yes, we did sing *Follow the Yellow Brick Road.*

It took me back to that production all those years ago. Did I mention that I was cast as Dorothy? I never got to play her, but Lucy did in 2022. She was fantastic.

My intuition had been right – it was the best production for years. On opening night I sat between Robert and Stella watching the timeless classic starring two generations of mine, and my granddaughter duetting with Robert's son. Now that's what I call Kismet! Ⓜ

Brain Boosters

Kriss Kross

Try to fit all of the listed words back into the grid.

4 letters
LEER
VIEW
VINE

5 letters
FLANK
HEADY

MYNAH
6 letters
ICONIC
MUTATE

7 letters
PITIFUL
UPGRADE

8 letters
CHARISMA
METEORIC

9 letters
EXEMPLARY
PLAINSONG

10 letters
ASYMMETRIC
CONFERENCE

11 letters
IMPERSONATE
MERITOCRACY

Turn To Page 173 For Solutions

Christmas Savings

What had their love added up to after all these years, Tess wondered? And what was its value to Michael?

By Marie Penman

PICTURES: SHUTTERSTOCK

Tess always enjoyed turning over the page on the big family calendar on the kitchen wall – a new month to plan for, full of possibilities! – apart from that final page from November to December.

Every year, without fail, this one induced a feeling of panic when she read the lines, *Less than four weeks to Christmas – yikes!*

This year was no different. There were already a few scribbled reminders in the calendar – last posting dates, Christmas

nights out – but Tess glanced instead at the sixteenth of the month, which fell on a Saturday this year.

She smiled to herself. This year would be a special anniversary.

On December the sixteenth, it would be exactly thirty years since she had first fallen in love with Michael, her husband. Back then he'd been just another colleague in the bank they both worked at.

As Tess put the calendar back on its hook, she ignored any feelings of panic over all the Christmas shopping still to be done, and instead allowed herself a few moments to reminisce.

Thirty years ago, she had just started working in the bank on a graduate trainee programme. Fresh out of

university and living in the city for the first time, she had felt like a grown-up at last, sharing a flat with two friends and getting the Tube into work each morning. To a job she quickly realised was not for her.

Tess had felt she didn't belong, among new colleagues who all seemed to be older and smarter than her, but she reasoned she had to try her best.

Then, the week before she broke off for the Christmas holidays, she had met Michael, and her world changed forever.

Their eyes met across a box of brown manila envelopes, as they both rummaged in the walk-in stationery cupboard on the third floor, Tess looking for new pay-in slips and Michael attempting to find financial planning guidance sheets and A5 envelopes. In the days before ➡

the internet, so much of life seemed to revolve around random pieces of paper.

She heard Michael before she saw him that day, talking to himself in the corner of the cupboard.

"Pretty sure they were on this shelf last time," he muttered. "Or was it on the opposite wall?"

Tess had smiled to herself, relieved that somebody else in the bank sounded as confused as she felt.

Then Michael had glanced up at her, his long, floppy fringe falling over his face, and she'd gasped at the sight of his dark blue eyes. Eyes that were unlike any others she'd seen before, almost navy in colour; eyes that would, in years to come, be repeated in two of their three children.

It was hard to imagine now, but before the days of email, dedicated staff had worked full-time in the bank's mailroom, sorting and delivering messages around the huge building.

Tess had never received anything in the internal mail before and had opened the envelope excitedly.

Inside, she was disappointed to see an A4 handout about financial planning for the future, and assumed it had come from the personnel department. Then she noticed there was writing on the back of the sheet.

Hello again, Tess in customer service! The bank has a Christmas party night booked for all staff on December 22 – details on the staffroom noticeboard.

Was he even aware of the significance of the date? Where would they be going?

He'd smiled at Tess and stopped pulling boxes from the shelves for a minute to introduce himself.

"Hi. I'm Michael from future investments, fourth floor," he'd grinned, formally shaking her hand.

Tess had smiled in return.

"Tess. I'm one of the graduate trainees, currently on rotation in customer service, new accounts."

Then they'd both just stood there, in the stationery cupboard, smiling at each other and at the sheer good fortune of them being in there at the same time.

The moment of magic – because that's what it had felt like to Tess – had lasted all of a minute, before Michael found what he was looking for.

They had mumbled shy goodbyes to each other, then the following day, as Tess continued to struggle with the intricacies of new account form-filling, an envelope had arrived in the internal mail.

Would you like to come with me that night? I promise we won't talk about anything bank-related. From Michael in future investments.

Tess had smiled in delight. He was asking her out! He'd felt the same as she did in the stationery cupboard!

Quickly, she'd scribbled a reply underneath Michael's invitation, and stuffed the handout back into the internal mail, still grinning to herself.

The following week, they'd had their first date at the Christmas night out, and Tess had loved Michael ever since.

But now, thirty years later, with both of them busy with work and their children and life itself, had that original Christmas magic faded just a little bit?

Tess sighed as she looked again at the calendar on the wall. December the sixteenth would always be a special date for her, but she wasn't sure Michael even remembered when they'd first met.

So much had changed since then.

Neither of them had lasted at the bank. Michael had retrained as a maths teacher, while Tess had stayed at home with the children – three babies in their first five years of marriage! – and had then concentrated on her art, producing watercolour paintings of the coastlines near their home.

Now their children were all grown up and while Tess still loved her life, she felt sorry for Michael. He still worked long, hard hours, getting stressed teaching children who seemed even less interested in maths than she had been in banking.

Over dinner that night, Michael had smiled at the new page on the calendar.

"Wow, I'd actually forgotten today was the first of December!" he said, helping himself to more pasta. "The countdown to Christmas is on."

Tess frowned. "I know it should be easier now that the kids are all older, but somehow, it isn't. So much to do!"

Michael looked at her, and his eyes, as usual, mesmerised her.

"Let's not get too flustered about Christmas this year, babes," he said. "And let's have a special night out together, just the two of us. What do you say?"

"That would be lovely." Tess was surprised by how pleased she felt.

Michael pulled a pen from his shirt pocket – red, used to mark endless homework jotters – and casually leaned over to the calendar on the wall.

Big night out, he scribbled in the blank space beside Saturday, December the sixteenth. Then he winked at Tess.

"I'll make all the arrangements – it'll be a surprise."

In the days and weeks that followed, Tess worked hard preparing gifts and artwork for Christmas, dealing with online orders and delivering parcels to the post office. Christmas was always her busiest time of year, yet she loved the idea of her work going out into the world.

In between times, she pondered the Big Night Out coming up and wondered what Michael had planned. Was he even aware of the significance of the date? Where would they be going?

She couldn't help but feel excited and ordered a new dress to wear, as well as booking herself a hair appointment for that morning.

A couple of days before the sixteenth, Michael sent her a text from work.

Forgot to say – it's an overnight stay on Saturday. Pack a bag, Mrs B!

Tess laughed, delighted that Michael could still surprise her like this. But where were they going and why was he being so secretive about it?

She asked the children if they knew what their dad was up to. Lucy grinned excitedly, but said she was sworn to secrecy. The two boys either didn't know a thing, or simply weren't interested.

The temperature dropped on December the fifteenth and on the day of the Big Night Out, it actually started snowing! Tess was like a child seeing Santa for the first time, bubbling with excitement as she headed out to get her hair done in the morning.

At two that afternoon, with Tess wrapped up in her new winter coat, her hair falling in silky, shiny layers across her shoulders, the two of them headed out.

The first surprise was that they drove only as far as the train station, where Michael carried their bag on to the platform and produced tickets for a trip into the city.

"We're going into the city?" yelped Tess. "Ooh, this is exciting! I've been desperate to see the Christmas lights!"

"There's a lot more excitement than that on the schedule." Michael grinned. ➡

Tess giggled, thinking how crazy it was that she still felt this way about her husband after so many years, and wondered if he felt the same. Men just weren't so sentimental about life and love.

In the city, Michael took the bag and held Tess's hand, leading her through the crowded streets under twinkling lights and past festive shop windows as fat flakes of snow fluttered through the air.

"Oh, look, Michael – we're close to the bank building! I hadn't realised we were in that area."

He led her across a square, down a side street and then through an alleyway until they were standing in front of a palatial hotel, decked in hundreds of tiny

"Come with me, Tess – I have something to show you."

They walked slowly down the sweeping staircase, in awe of the décor and all they ways it was different but still the same as the old bank, until they came to a small side room on the third floor. There was a tiny cocktail bar, with just a couple of tables and chairs, and Michael ordered a bottle of Champagne for them.

Tess looked around. Could this possibly be…? Was it the same room?

Michael gave Tess her Champagne and held up his glass in a toast to her.

"To you, Tess," he said, smiling at his wife. "Thirty years ago today, I saw you for the first time – in the stationery cupboard on the third floor.

Michael watched his wife, enjoying her look of amazement and surprise

white lights and festive wreaths, with silver bells and Christmas trees around the entrance way. Tess gasped.

"Wait. Isn't this our bank building?"

Michael watched his wife, enjoying the look of amazement and surprise on her face, still beautiful after all these years.

"It's now called the Old Bank Hotel – and it's where we're staying tonight."

Tess laughed and threw her arms around Michael's neck.

"No way! When did this happen? How did you know?" she asked.

Michael smiled.

"I read a newspaper article about the renovation work. Come on, let's get checked in before we freeze!"

Their room on the fifth floor was just perfect – warm, luxurious, and with views over the city skyline – and later that evening, once Tess had changed for dinner and before they headed out, Michael took her by the hand again.

"I know it sounds a bit corny, but I really think I fell in love with you at that exact moment."

Tess's eyes filled with tears as she looked at this man who meant everything to her, who without having referred to it at all during their marriage, had the same memory of their first meeting as she did.

Michael reached into the inside pocket of his blazer and produced a piece of paper. It was faded and a little crumpled, but Tess could still make out the wording at the top: the faded letters referring to financial planning for the future.

"I've kept this the whole time, Tess, to remind me that even though my career in banking didn't work out, I made the best investment of my life here."

And then he leaned over and kissed her softly on the lips, reminding Tess all over again just why she loved this man so very much.

The magic of Christmas lived on. MW

RECIPE AND FOOD STYLING: JENNIE SHAPTER PHOTOGRAPHY: JON WHITAKER

Plum And Almond Crumble

Ingredients (Serves 2)

- ◆ **350g ripe red plums, halved and stoned**
- ◆ **2-3tbsp caster sugar**

For the topping:

- ◆ **50g plain flour**
- ◆ **50g butter, cut into cubes**
- ◆ **40g rolled oats**
- ◆ **15g flaked almonds**
- ◆ **40g light brown sugar**
- ◆ **½tsp ground cinnamon**
- ◆ **Custard or cream, to serve, optional**

1 Preheat the oven to 190°C, fan 170°C, Gas Mark 5. Cut the plum halves in half and place in a 750-800ml ovenproof dish. Sprinkle over the sugar, add more or less according to how sweet you like your fruit. Toss together.

2 Place the flour in a bowl, add the butter and rub in until it resembles fine breadcrumbs. Stir in the oats, almonds, brown sugar and cinnamon. Spread over the plums and bake for 25-30 minutes. For a single serving, bake for 20 minutes. Serve with cream or custard, if wished.

Something To Unwrap

What do you buy for kids who have everything... or who have nothing? It seems both are tricky to get right

By Alison Carter

PICTURES: SHUTTERSTOCK

None of the Mostons had a problem with the family about to move into the granny flat, or with Kim's decision to rent it out under the scheme.

"But it is nearly Christmas, remember," her husband Neil said, "so it's extra for the list."

They were a large family – four kids – but their house was big and rambling. Granny Moston was not yet ready for

the two-bedroom extension attached to the side. The Mostons were preparing to rent the flat to a family recently granted refugee status.

Neil read through the scheme details as December rain hammered on the kitchen window.

"You have to hand it to them," he said. "This is well-organised. There's vetting, preparation to make sure they're good tenants, and this deposit bond thing."

"They're unlikely to have brought savings, fleeing Sudan."

"And there's ongoing support," Neil said. He looked up. "It's all a bit… real."

"It is," Kim replied with a nervous smile. "This afternoon we'll tackle the

flat. The little bedroom needs a clear-out. Remember, we're landlords, but just in a particular way."

The decision had been a natural one. None of the children were permanently at home now. They were at university, or travelling. It wasn't about needing extra money, because they had plenty, with Kim's good insurance job and Neil's food packaging business.

It was just an interesting thing to do, and an opportunity to contribute.

Kim took the sheaf of print-outs from her husband.

Before all that," she said, "Christmas presents. If we don't talk about that, it will be too late again, and they are all going ➔

to be home. To be honest, I'm thinking about cash for the kids this year."

Neil pouted. "I bet you'll give in. I bet we'll eventually be scrabbling around in shops for something they want, something they'll actually use."

"Ha! An impossible task."

Neil and Kim got the flat ready, and one cold Thursday, three nervous individuals arrived with two rucksacks and a plastic bag.

The young parents had a smattering of English; the little boy, Abdo, quite a bit more. They had been in the UK for a while, but looked shellshocked because, once their refugee status was granted, they'd had just twenty-eight days to find accommodation.

"We have three aunts between us who already enough scarves and boxes of truffles to sink the Titanic."

"As I said, money is best for the kids."

"Paid into their bank accounts on Christmas Eve? Ugh."

Neil groaned.

The children came back – Tom first from university, then Kerry from Berlin where she seemed to have acquired not one but two boyfriends, then Hal.

They all greeted the Ajak family, and Tom began to form a hesitant relationship with the little boy, who was ten.

Kerry asked if the Ajaks would come round on Christmas Day.

"I know they're not Christians, but…"

Neil and Kim looked at each other. Kim could tell that the idea had been in

"How about we get Hal golf clubs? That would provide years of themed gifts"

The first hours were awkward – Kim trying too hard and Neil persuading her to leave Abdo, Kamal and Hiba alone.

Later, Kim sat in the kitchen fretting about whether the flat's heating was turned up too high, and would they understand the thermostat, and did they really know where Tesco was?

"They're going to be fine," Neil said.

To distract her, he brought out the Christmas list.

He bemoaned the fact that there wasn't a single "easy" person on it to buy presents for.

"We used to have Uncle Carl, guaranteed to love his bottle of whisky, but he went and died."

"He was ninety-seven," Kim said.

"Now I have you to buy for – and that's a nightmare. We have four children who choose their own jeans, and buy their own phones, and no longer need Lego.

Neil's mind, too.

"We'll ask," she said.

On the sixteenth of December, Kim caved in about presents for the kids. She made Neil drive with her to Bluewater Shopping Centre. She was laughing as she climbed into the car.

"I knew I wouldn't be able to cope with the empty floor under the tree."

"I should have bet you fifty quid that you'd give in," Neil said.

Their shopping began enthusiastically enough, with circuits of each floor of the department store (except Furniture and Baby), but quickly they began to struggle.

Eventually, Kim found a perfume that Kerry had worn as a teenager.

"Ironic," she said firmly, dropping it into the basket. "Nostalgia value."

"Will she use it?"

Kim bit her lip. "Not sure about that."

The boys were impossible. Kim and Neil tossed the usual ideas back and forth – a belt, socks, a leather washbag. But Tom was vegan now, and Hal was earning well and picked his own luxury goods.

They found a shop dedicated to gifts for men, but everything on sale seemed to be golf-themed.

"How about we get Hal golf clubs?" Neil said with a sigh. "That would provide years of themed gifts stretching into the future."

In the end they bought edible presents for both boys – spices, Turkish delight, a bread-making kit and some pointless mini games and gimmicky books. For Kerry, they added in earrings that looked like some she already owned, and a bottle of posh body lotion.

They stopped for tea and sat back, exhausted.

"Good grief, First World problems," Kim said, "trying to spend money!"

Neil sat up.

"Hang on. What about Abdo, Kamal and Hiba?"

Kerry had persuaded them to come round for coffee and Christmas cake on Christmas morning. They felt this wouldn't be overwhelming.

Having said that, Kamal and Hiba Ajak were proving to be a lively, forward-thinking pair, full of plans.

Kamal already had a job, and Hiba was chasing her son around, prepping him as much as she could for school in January. They had nothing at all, and were beginning all over again (the truth of that made Kim feel breathless sometimes), but they had determination.

"Oh. Yeah!" Kim said. "There has to be something under the tree for them to unwrap, especially for Abdo."

They agreed that the presents should be modest – a sign of welcome rather than anything which carried expectations of gifts in return, or something ostentatious and therefore embarrassing.

They set off for the toy shop to see what might work for Abdo. The task was harder than they expected, with the huge and overwhelming displays of plastic and electronics, but after a quarter of an hour Neil called Kim to the back of the shop.

"Remember these?" he said.

He was in the kids' stationery section, looking at the sets of drawing and painting stuff that Kerry, Tom and Hal had loved when they were Abdo's age and younger.

"I say 'loved'," Neil said thoughtfully. "They fell on them with cries of delight on Christmas morning when they were six, but months later I'd find them, two crayons missing, the watercolours a bit mucky, and the rest untouched."

"I'm embarrassed at how many of those ended up in the bin," Kim said.

A stationery set seemed acceptable for Abdo; no parent could have a problem with that. Neil and Kim spent their last half hour on Hiba and Kamal, and drove home satisfied.

Christmas morning arrived, and the Mostons got round the fire early to hand out presents.

It was the usual thing – polite comments about Kim's new vase sent by an absent aunt (she had dozens of vases), Hal's snort of laughter at a T-shirt from his brother with an insulting slogan, which everybody knew he wouldn't wear.

Kerry was lovely about the earrings, but Kim was not convinced she'd wear them after Boxing Day.

They all knew they had over-catered massively, stocking up with enough "standby" dessert and "just in case" pork pies, Stilton and vegan alternatives to feed a small nation.

The Ajaks arrived promptly, smiling and wearing their Sunday best. Kim ➤

took Hiba into the kitchen to make hot drinks.

"Oh dear," Hiba said as the fridge door swung open and three cartons of yogurt bounced across the floor. The fridge was hopelessly overloaded.

"Sorry," Kim said, blushing, jamming the yogurts back in and grabbing an eight-pint container of semi-skimmed.

They re-entered the lounge with teas, coffees and Christmas cake, just as Tom got down on his hands and knees to pull a long, flat parcel from under the tree.

He held it out to Abdo, who smiled and nodded his appreciation of the handsome tartan paper and the navy-blue bow.

"No – it's a present for you, Abdo," Tom said. "Here."

lifted it clear, so carefully that the room stood still. He touched the sharpener, the three brushes in size order, the bright red disc of paint that marked the start of the row of colours, then the yellow. He put the cover back on as though re-sealing the Ark of the Covenant.

Kim's mind went back again to her children's earliest days when they had known wonder. Those days had been short-lived because they'd had everything whenever they needed it – every Christmas and in between. She and Neil had never wanted to spoil them; it was just that they were lucky people.

For Abdo, this gift was a very big deal: he had so little, and for many years of his young life he had been in a camp.

She was about to say, "It's nothing," but stopped herself. This was not nothing

The room fell strangely quiet. Kim wondered if she had made a mistake in buying gifts, but it was too late.

"It's just a token," Neil said. Instinctively, Kim silenced him with a hand on his arm.

Abdo stepped forward slowly, and hesitated as Tom held the parcel out further towards him. He took it, knelt with it on the carpet and looked up at his dad, who nodded. Abdo undid the sticky tape and peeled off the paper, until the stationery set was revealed. To Kim, it looked tackier than it had in the shop among all the other the consumer goods – its plastic cover flimsy, the eraser too small, with too much variety. It was gimmicky, and she thought again of the discarded sets from her children's past Christmases. She swallowed.

She saw that Abdo was holding his breath. He ran three fingers along the transparent cover, reached the end and

There, eating and staying well were a daily challenge; frivolous presents were not even a thought in parents' minds.

Abdo stood up, keeping the stationery set perfectly parallel with the floor. He walked over to Neil and said thank you, and then over to Kim and thanked her.

She was about to say, "It's nothing", but stopped herself. This was not nothing.

Abdo was looking at weeks – months – of creativity and fun. This present really meant something. Presents had not meant much in their house for a long time.

The Ajaks spent a happy two hours round the tree, then went back to their flat. The Mostons were quiet as they made lunch. They left the rest of the unwrapped presents under the tree for later.

Kerry stood stirring the bread sauce.

"That's what a Christmas present is about," she said.

And no one needed to ask which present she meant. Ⓜ

Dear Mrs Claus

Ho, ho, ho dear – all is not jolly at the North Pole. And things are going to get worse before they get better…

By Lauren Rebbeck

Dear Mrs Claus,
I'm so-so-so sorry. (Hoping that sounded as charming as it did in my head.) But you know better than anyone how manic things get during December… it's why we had to wait until January 1 to get hitched in the first place!

Until that sleigh's reparked in the grotto's garage and I can shove that itchy red suit in the wash, I can't think about anything other than The Big Day.

But that's no excuse, I should have remembered *our* big day.

I mean, I did remember it! I just kept getting distracted. The Wi-Fi kept cutting out, you see, and I was trying to connect to a Zoom meeting about whether Dylan N should be on the naughty or nice list →

this year – so it truly was an emergency.

I never thought you'd leave.

Don't you want to come home? You do tend to clash with that neat freak cousin of yours. I'm still getting over that telling-off I got for rolling up the toothpaste tube when we stayed for Easter weekend.

about it. And physical. I've got the biggest bruise on my thigh from a snowball that Frosty hurled this afternoon.

I'm having to run past them to get to the workshop without being pelted – and I don't know if you've noticed, but I'm not as fit as I once was.

Since you've been away, no one's been checking that the elves brush their teeth

But OK, I suppose she is the Tooth Fairy – and I'm not exactly in a position to lecture anyone for bringing their work home with them, am I?

Come home, and we can celebrate our anniversary together once all the Christmas hoo-ha is over with.

Sent with love/checked twice,
Mr Claus

Dear Mrs Claus,
Could you ask your cousin to make an emergency dental appointment for Crinkles from Gift Wrapping? He's chipped his tooth on a candy cane!

Come home soon.

Sent with love/checked twice,
Mr Claus

P.S. Shimmer from Christmas Lights Division has just informed me that since you've been away, no one's been checking that the elves brush their teeth before bed… or supervised them around the leftover advent calendar chocolates.

Ask Tooth Fairy to keep a few more appointment spaces open, will you?

Dear Mrs Claus,
This cold shoulder is icier than the sleigh's windscreen. (Do you know where we keep the de-icer, by the way?)

It's not just you, either. Everyone is angry with me about our separation.

The snowmen have been very vocal

Speaking of cardio, how on earth do you find the time and energy to take those reindeer for a nine-mile hike every day? I'm exhausted. I don't know how you do it.

I miss talking over the plans for the Big Day and gossiping with you about all the goings-on here at the North Pole.

There's a new romance baking in Mince Pie Division… I'll tell you all about that if you write back! Or better yet, if you come home.

Sent with love/checked twice,
Mr Claus

P.S. I hope you like the diamond snowflake earrings.

Dear Mrs Claus,
What's the password for our online account at Iceland? No one ordered the big shop, and you don't want to be around elves with low blood sugar. I need an urgent bulk lot of frozen chicken nuggets!

Sent with love/checked twice,
Mr Claus

Dear Mrs Claus,
It's lonely in the Arctic Circle without you, my Jingle Belle. Half the elves can't talk to me because they have toothache. The snowmen only shout at me.

And now, the reindeer won't talk to me because I bought the wrong brand of kibble. They said the one I got tastes like cardboard and sprouts. Prancer thinks the

one you buy is carrot flavoured, but Vixen is adamant that it's parsnip.

I hope you like the gingerbread portrait I made of you. Even in biscuit form, you are beautiful.

Piping your likeness in icing made me realise I've let myself go over the years. Somewhere along the way, it stopped being about filling the Santa boots, and more about over-filling the suit.

Truth be told, I can't actually fit down the chimneys of some of the terraced houses any more.

But I think I've lost a couple of pounds with all the reindeer hikes and running from snowball assassination attempts. I've even gone down a hole on my big black belt. Oh, and I've been hitting the grotto gym! Yep, I've dusted off those candy cane weights, and even thrown the old bags of coal around.

Maybe when you come home, we can work out together?

But let's just work this out first.
Sent with love/checked twice,
Mr Claus

Dear Mrs Claus,
There's been a huge blizzard in the North Pole this week, the worst storm I've seen since our wedding day.

I remember all those years ago, pacing at the altar, the hail pounding on the tin roof. I was worrying about your sleigh making it through all that snow, and terrified you'd skidded off the road.

Then, boom! The chapel doors flew open, and there you were. A vision in a white ski suit and spiked snowshoes. Your beautiful face pink from the cold, veil flapping behind you in the wind.

You would go to the ends of the earth (in snowshoes) for the people you love.

It's not the same, but I hope you like the snow globe I made for you. I know you think they make you look old, but ➜

make sure you put your glasses on when you take a look. Right there inside that soapy blizzard is a tiny version of us on our wedding day.

I want you to remember forever how happy we were that day. Even if I can't make you happy right now.

Give it a shake and remember, my love.
Sent with love/checked twice,
Mr Claus

Dear Mrs Claus,
Day three of the blizzard. I'm exhausted. The roof of the stables has blown off, and the elves are terrified. Without you here, they've got extremely clingy and follow me around all day like baby penguins. They even insist on sleeping in our bed at night!

Everyone's too miserable and tired to get anything done. We're dangerously behind schedule. And to top it all off, I've put my back out. I was sleeping in the bathtub, since the elves have taken over our bed. But last night, Comet and Cupid came creeping in looking more sheepish than reindeerish. They ended up commandeering the bathtub, and I was relegated to the floor.

The ice pack is doing nothing for my backache. Or should I be using the hot water bottle?

Dear Mrs Claus,
The skies have finally brightened, but the days are still dull without you.

I took the whole grotto along for the reindeer hike today, thinking it would do them all good to get some fresh air. It ended in tears and a rather violent snowball fight. The entire Gift Wrap Division is now grounded.

Could you ask Tooth Fairy to fit Sparkle in tomorrow for an emergency denture fitting? Front two teeth.

Please, PLEASE come home!
Sent with love/checked twice,
Mr Claus

Dear Mrs Claus,
I understand why you had to leave. You need eyes in the back of your head, four pairs of arms and the patience of a saint to run this madhouse. I don't know how you do it so flawlessly. With a smile.

I lost it today. I could hear them squabbling in the workshop all the way from the gym. I had to get out.

I think the delivery man squished our shipment of marshmallows on purpose

I just don't have the right words to make them all feel better, and tell them it's going to be OK, when the truth is that I don't know if it will be.

I wish you were back in our bed. I'll even keep sleeping in the bathtub if you aren't ready to share the covers with me. Just please come home.

Sent with love/checked twice,
Mr Claus
P.S. Where do you get that peppermint-flavoured paracetamol from?

So, I went off the usual reindeer trail into the clearing by Holly Berry Hill where we had that picnic on our first anniversary. The mistletoe was in full bloom. I sat below the poplar trees where we carved our initials and listened to the quiet. Nothing but a pair of little robins, carolling together.

Maybe when you get back, we could hike out there together? Take a couple of turkey sandwiches and some hot apple cider, maybe.

They're still there – our initials. As clear as the day we etched them all those decades ago. *S.C. loves M.S.*

That carving will never fade, and neither will my love.

Sent with love/checked twice,
Mr Claus

P.S. I picked you these snowdrops from the clearing.

Dear Mrs Claus,
The North Pole isn't home without you. The reindeer are too skinny. The snowmen are surly. The elves are sassy and sugar-fuelled.

It's only December 29 and we're already three times over the tinsel budget, because no one can balance the books like you. There's a huge scorch mark on the bum of my best velvet trousers – I burned them on that finnicky iron I got you last Christmas. (Also, I'm sorry for getting you an iron for Christmas.)

I think the delivery man squished our shipment of marshmallows for the cocoa on purpose, he's got a bit of a sweet spot for you. And I can't blame him.

I had a Zoom call with the directors of that new Santa Claus movie they're working on, and we were discussing who should play you. I told them it must be someone sophisticated yet sexy, like Helen Mirren. But even she can't hold an advent candle to you, my turtle dove.

Sent with love/checked twice,
Mr Claus

Dear Mrs Claus,
Everyone's mad at me. Everyone misses you. But the silver lining of the entire North Pole giving me the silent treatment is that I've had time to reflect.

We've had no time for ourselves in years! Too many leaping lords, piping pipers and bloomin' birds hanging around! We need some time to just be man and wife, not Mr and Mrs Claus. We need to focus on each other too – not only the two billion children in the world.

Which is why, for our anniversary on New Years Eve, I have arranged for the elves to have a sleepover at Easter Bunny's warren.

The grotto will be completely empty of glittery, sugar-charged dependants, but full of twinkly fairy lights, and the smell of fresh baked stollen. I'll roast my famous cinnamon-crusted turkey and make that extra-sweet cranberry sauce you like. Bublé's giving us a private concert (he owes me a favour.)

Then we can pop open that vintage bottle of mulled wine… and maybe even take a dip in the frozen lake, like we used to when we first got married.

We can see in the New Year right – start as we mean to go on.

So, please come home for our anniversary. We can celebrate timeless romance on New Year's Eve, and a fresh start on New Year's Day. I can't wait to fall in love with you all over again,
Mr Claus

Dear Mr Claus,
I love that idea. And I love you. No matter how many notches we drill into your belt, one way or another.

My Ski-Doo arrives at midnight – can you can pick me up at the station? I have a few suitcases I'll need help lifting, so we can put your new muscles to the test.

Thank you for all the beautiful gifts you sent. I've picked up a few for you too. Tooth Fairy took me shopping in Valentine's Village, and let's just say, it might actually be a good thing you're on my naughty list this year, Mr Claus.

Get ready for fireworks in the North Pole this New Year's Eve.

Yours forever,
Mrs Claus MW

Each Week For You To Enjoy

My Weekly

Amazing Cookery

Favourite Celebrities

Up-to-date Health News

Fabulous Fiction

Your Feel Good Read

PLUS

◆ **Puzzles** ◆ **Fashion** ◆ **Beauty** ◆ **Real Life**

You'll Love It!
On Sale Every Tuesday